FLORIDA'S GEOLOGICAL TREASURES

BY
IRIS TRACY COMFORT

Baldwin Park, California
GEM GUIDES BOOK CO.
1998

NOTE: *Due to the possibility of personal error, typographical error, misinterpretation of information, and the many changes due to man or nature,* Florida's Geological Treasures, *its publisher, and all other persons directly or indirectly associated with this publication, assume no responsibility for accidents, injury, or any losses by individuals or groups using this publication. Sites listed in this book are intended only as statements of mineral occurrence and in no way imply that collecting there is either non-hazardous or legal, without the express permission of the owner.*

Gem Guides Book Co.
315 Cloverleaf Dr., Suite F
Baldwin Park, CA 91706

Book typography and binding design by Art Waxer Designs, Berkeley, California

Manufactured in the United States of America

TABLE OF CONTENTS

ILLUSTRATIONS

An eight-page section of color photographs
is bound in between pages 64 and 65.

ACKNOWLEDGEMENTS

With deep appreciation for their help

Arthur Theodor Weber, Diplom-Ingenieurs, Bergakademie, Germany, mentor and guide.

The staff at Florida Geological Survey in Tallahassee: Dr. Walter Schmidt, Ph.D., P.G., State Geologist and Chief; Dr. Thomas H. Scott, Ph. D., P.G., Assistant State Geologist for Geological Investigations; Steven M. Spencer, P.G., Economic Geologist; Geologist Ed Lane, members of the library staff, to name only a few. I'm grateful for your time, the vast amount of information you made available, and for the photos shared.

Fellow troglodytes I have known through almost 25 years as a member of the National Speleology Society.

Fellow members of Florida Mineral Friends, and to fellow members of the Central Florida Mineral and Gem Society in Orlando and its affiliate, the Eastern Federation of Mineralogical and Lapidary Societies. For sharing your expertise and collecting sites, and fellowship, thank you!

Dr. Mark Stewart, Chairman, Geology Department U.S.F. for time and help; to Dr. Frank Kujawa, U.C.F. for special insights and introductions; to Florida State Museum for help and direction given through the years.

Bernard L. Murowchick, Consulting Mineralogist, for hospitality and time and sharing his fantastic knowledge of phosphate minerals as well as his mineral collection.

Photographer Dan Behnke and geologist-photographer Anthony Gricius, whose stunning photographs of secondary phosphate minerals, nationally honored, appear in the center folio of this book. And to Michael M. Smith, known throughout Florida for his excellent environmental TV documentaries, whose black and white photos appear on many of these pages.

Author's Guild and Helen McGrath with many thanks for their help.

Eugenia Wright, Pat Phillips, Barbara Sanders and Mel Phillips who were always there when I needed them.

Special love and appreciation and thanks to son Alain for his insights and so much more.

Everyone who shared geological collections and locations, time, expertise, experience, information! There isn't enough space to name each of you nor to tell you how very much I do cherish you!

Chapter 1

WHAT CAN YOU FIND?

T HE SCOPE of rocks and minerals you can find in Florida is one of this state's big surprises. What geological collectibles offer themselves on this peninsula thrust out between the Atlantic Ocean and the Gulf of Mexico? More than you might think at first glance! A quick overview may offer you a number of surprises.

Sand? Of course. But you'll be amazed when you read what you can find in that sand. Shells? Some of them shelter creatures still alive—and some shells nearby are million-year-old fossil remains of creatures long dead.

That is just the beginning of Florida's wonders. Once you really take a look around, the picture enlarges. Did you know that Florida ranks fifth among the mining states in the United States? Minerals are to be found in Florida in abundance. And caves with beautiful formations. And quarry cuts that expose hardened layers like rich rock showcases. And coral forests that lie just off-shore.

Some rock formations in the state have great commercial value. As you study the maps in this book, especially ones that show the geology of specific regions of Florida, you will find several fuller's earth mines in the north of Florida. Limestone, phosphate, chert, kaolin, and gypsum are scattered through the state.

Florida is a source of such rare minerals as zirconium and titanium. Zircon and limonite are found here, too. Flint, a small amount of iron, glorious layers of chalcedony—which line certain fossilized coral and bal-

7

last rock no longer needed and therefore dumped from ships all over the world—are also to be found.

At Gainesville, Florida's share of America's basement rock is closest to the surface—3000 feet below it. Granite has been drilled in Osceola County at close to that depth. But you can be almost positive that if you find a piece of granite on the surface in Florida, it has been shipped or carried in from outside the state.

Another great treasure of Florida lies in the wondrous number and variety of fossils to be discovered. No record written compares to the ancient true tales of Florida creatures dead millions of years, their history a blink in the eye of time, their records preserved for you to read and collect. Among Florida's most spellbinding stories are the stories written in rock.

There are older rocks than Florida's in these United States, of course. The crust of our planet is presently estimated around three thousand million years old. In contrast, the very oldest of South Florida's rock, Tamiami Limestone, was formed only six million years ago. Some other Florida limestone formations are just 100,000 years old, by comparison. Geologists tend to consider most of southern Florida's rocks very young— among the country's youngest.

EARTHQUAKES

Underneath Florida is the North American plate, the same huge block of rock that underlies most of our continent. This block of rock has major faults or fractures in other parts of the United States, but mostly minor ones in Florida. Enormous and complex forces and stresses are responsible for earthquakes generally, among them the shifting of great fractures. Because Florida is on the trailing edge of the North American plate, few earthquakes occur in Florida.

Still, Florida has had earthquakes. Two in particular, the New Madrid Earthquake of 1811-1812 and the Charleston Earthquake of 1886, were noteworthy even though neither epicenter was located in the state. The famous New Madrid Earthquake had an epicenter located near New Madrid, Missouri. It produced bizarre effects in Missouri and a large part of Arkansas and caused the Mississippi River to flow backward for a time— reported variously from a few hours to several days. That quake affected a great part of the United States east of the Mississippi. In Florida, temblors shook the western part of the peninsula's panhandle.

The Charleston Earthquake of 1886 did not originate in Florida either, but its effects certainly were felt in that state. Newspapers from 1886, among them the Florida *Times-Union,* of Jacksonville, carried colorful accounts of the Charleston Earthquake that began the evening of August 31 and produced severe shocks along the eastern seaboard as far north as

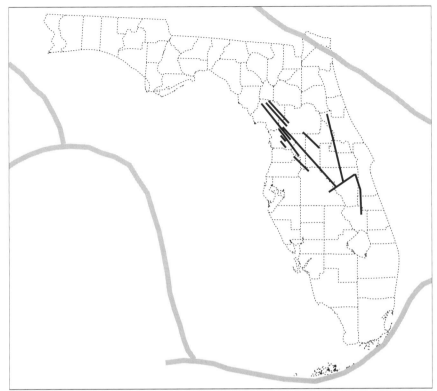

Fault lines in Florida, from the U.S. Geological Survey map of young faults in the U.S. The broad gray lines indicate the boundaries of fault regions; black lines are suspected fault lines.

New York and as far south as Key West.

Florida's experience began with a tidal wave that came in off the coast and smashed down the St. Johns River past Mayport. Jacksonville was just a few miles away to the west. The city began to shake, people began to run frantically into the streets, and boats and ships rocked violently in the harbor as waves leaped. The Florida *Times-Union* reported a brilliant red glare over the Wakulla swamps as gas from underground natural deposits caught fire and lighted up the night skies. From September 1 through September 4, 1886, the *Times-Union* published accounts of the earthquake, some written while shocks were actually occurring.

In his report *Earthquakes and Seismic History of Florida* for the Florida Geological Survey, Ed Lane says, "Of the earthquakes felt in Florida, only six are considered to have had epicenters in Florida, and even some of these were possibly the effects of tremors from earthquakes outside Florida."

Lane compiled a list of earthquakes "felt" in various parts of Florida. In this list he suggested using a modified **Mercalli Scale,** written as **MM,** rather than the Richter scale, to measure intensity, since the Mercalli scale is based on actual human observations and is therefore more meaningful. Mercalli scale values of shock intensities are given as Roman numerals and range from **MM I** to **MM XII.** Most of the earthquakes felt in Florida had estimated local intensities of **MM IV** to **MM VI.**

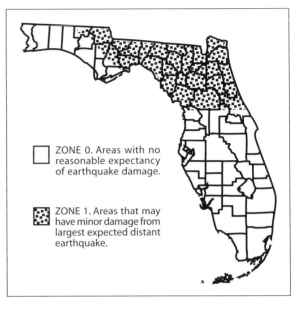

ZONE 0. Areas with no reasonable expectancy of earthquake damage.

ZONE 1. Areas that may have minor damage from largest expected distant earthquake.

An **MM IV** tremor is defined as: felt indoors by man, outdoors by a few. It may awaken light sleepers, rattle windows and glassware. It may cause houses to creak. An **MM VI** intensity tremor is felt by everyone, indoors or outdoors. It awakens all sleepers, frightens many people, creates general excitement, causes people to move unsteadily. Trees shake slightly, liquids move strongly, and there is damage to some buildings. Church bells ring, windows break, pictures and books fall, and furniture overturns.

A list compiled by Ed Lane of known earthquakes and "tremors" felt in Florida from 1727 through 1991, with estimated epicenters and intensities, provides a fascinating glimpse of the state's earthquake history:

October 29, 1727	Unofficial sources reported a severe quake **MM VI** in St. Augustine. (Original record not located.) New England had a severe shock about 10:40 a.m. on this date; a quake was reported on the island of Martinique the same day.
February 6, 1780	Pensacola felt a tremor described as "mild."
May 8, 1781	Pensacola suffered a "severe" tremor that shook ammunition racks from barrack walls and

leveled houses, but caused no fatalities.

February 8, 1843   Earthquake in West Indies, felt in the United States. Intensity is unknown.

January 12, 1879   Earthquake felt through north and central Florida, bounded by a line drawn from Fort Myers to Daytona on the south, to a line drawn from Tallahassee to Savannah, Georgia on the north, an area of about 23,000 square miles. Intensity **MM VI** near Gainesville.

January 22-23, 1880   Earthquake in Cuba of intensity **MM VII** east of Havana. It was felt in Florida.

January 27, 1880   Several shocks, **MM VII** to **MM VIII** were felt in Key West resulting from a disastrous earthquake at Vuelta Abajo, 80 miles west of Havana.

August 31, 1886   The great earthquake in Charleston, South Carolina, **MM X**. It was felt all over north Florida, with an estimated intensity of **MM V - MM VI**. Bells rang in St. Augustine, and severe shocks were felt along the east coast. Quake effects were felt in Tampa.

September 1-9, 1886   Jacksonville felt more aftershocks of intensity about **MM IV** from the Charleston quake.

November 5, 1886   Jacksonville felt another aftershock from the Charleston quake.

June 20, 1893   Jacksonville felt a tremor at 10:07 p.m. Estimated intensity was **MM IV.**

October 31, 1900   The U.S. Coast and Geodetic Survey recorded a local shock of **MM V** at Jacksonville.

January 23, 1903   A shock of intensity **MM VI** was felt at Savannah. Effects felt in north Florida.

June 12, 1912   A strong shock was felt at Savannah. Intensity is unknown. It was felt in Florida.

June 20, 1912 A **MM V** at Savannah, probably associated with the quake of June 12. It was felt in north Florida.

1930
Exact date
unknown

An earth tremor was felt over a wide area in central Florida near LaBelle, Fort Myers, and Marco Island. It was an earthquake but some believed it to be a tremendous explosion—no basis for this belief. Intensity at Marco Island: **MM V.**

January 19, 1942 Several shocks were felt on south coast Florida with some felt near Lake Okeechobee and in the Fort Myers area. Estimated intensity was **MM IV.**

January 5, 1945 About 10 a.m. windows shook violently in the De Land Courthouse, Volusia County.

December 22, 1945 A shock was felt in Miami Beach, Hollywood area at 11:25 a.m. Intensity was **MM I** to **MM III.**

November 8, 1948 A sudden jar, accompanied by sounds like distant explosions, rattled doors and windows on Captiva Island, west of Fort Myers.

November 18, 1952 Windows and doors were rattled by a slight tremor at Quincy, about 20 miles northwest of Tallahassee.

March 26, 1953 Two shocks estimated as **MM IV** were felt in the Orlando area.

October 27, 1973 A shock was felt in the central east coastal area of Seminole, Volusia, Orange, and Brevard Counties, at 1:21 a.m. Maximum intensity was **MM V.**

December 4, 1975 A shock was felt in Daytona and Orlando areas, 6:57 a.m. Maximum intensity was **MM IV.**

January 13, 1978	Two shocks were reported by residents in eastern Polk County, south of Haines City. Tremors were about one minute apart and each lasted about 15 seconds, shaking doors and rattling windows. They occurred between 4:10 and 4:20 p.m. There were no injuries or damages.
November 13, 1978	Tremors were felt in parts of northwest Florida near Lake City. The seismic station at Americus, Georgia, estimated it originated in the Atlantic Ocean.

"If it were not for the effects of the major earthquake of 1886 at Charleston," Ed Lane has said, "all of Florida would be in Zone O of the shaded Seismic Risk Map," on page 10. Since the Charleston earthquake is a colorful fact in Florida's history, however, the Seismic Risk Map shows almost a third of Florida in Zone 1.

COLLECTING

Whether you choose to collect actual geological specimens or to collect your specimens with a camera or a sketch pad, you have a wide choice of sites in Florida. The coastline stretches for 1,350 miles, the longest of any in the United States except Alaska and the Hawaiian Islands. Along this coast you can make a fine collection of coastal sand and collectible fossils in some areas. You can find heavy mineral deposits washed up at the high-tide line, and you can view some 50 varieties of coral in south Florida.

In Florida Caverns State Park in the north of Florida, there are stalagmites and stalactites and other cave formations to be photographed or sketched. Because this is a state park and protected by law, you will not be able to collect actual specimens here. However, there are other privately owned, less spectacular caves in this area where discreet collecting has been permitted. Nothing may be touched or taken without the owner's permission, of course. In the Appendix you will find copies of recent Florida legislation regarding parks and caves and collecting.

At the opposite end of the state is the John Pennekamp Coral Reef State Park with its underwater marvels, which are also under the protection of the park service and the law as far as collecting is concerned. You can ride in a glass-bottom boat for a spectacular view of the only living reef formation along the coasts of the continental United States.

Desirable specimens for collections sometimes appear in the most unlikely places. Just last year a friend came upon a trove of beautiful

Stalactites and stalagmites in a cave at Florida Caverns State Park. (Florida Geological Survey)

well-formed crystals as she walked alongside a road under construction to the east of Orlando. Road-building equipment had cut into a bed of crystalline material, and some of it contained clusters of very nice crystals.

There were enough specimens there for an entire city—but there was a catch. In a short time the piles of earth displaying these easily obtained crystals would be leveled and a concrete road would cover the find for the lifetime of the concrete. Time and crystals do not wait on road-builders. When you are lucky enough to find such a temporary situation, ask permission to collect immediately, make sure conditions are safe, then gather your specimens, protect them, and carry them off. Some prize materials require an investment of a lot of work and a bit of luck.

There are many places where you can find what you want for your collection. As we go along we will discuss what is to be found and the equipment that might help you find your specimens and protect and display them. We will also discuss the amenities that you should observe when dealing with the owners of property on which collectibles may be located.

LIGHTNING

One danger in Florida that must be addressed up front is lightning. Lightning anywhere is a hazard that must be respected, but in Florida it ranks as a major safety threat. The frequency of lightning strikes in Florida exceeds that of any state in the country, according to lightning experts. On a map produced by Texas A&M University, which shows lightning strike frequency throughout the United States, no other state registered in the seven strikes per one square kilometer range. Additionally, except for the far western part of the Panhandle and an extremely small bit of the southern zone of Florida, all of Florida is in the high seven- to thirteen- range. The area where the most intense lightning activity occurs is slightly northeast of Tampa, south to eastern Manatee and Sarasota counties.

Conditions that produce lightning are humidity and hot sun. The summer rainy season in Florida has an abundance of both. When thunderclouds build, get out of the open where you present a target and head for shelter—not under trees, of course. If you are wading, get out of the water, and if you are in a small boat, head for shore and shelter. The beach, too, is a dangerous place to be in a thunderstorm. These are the same precautions you would take anywhere in the country; in Florida they are absolutely essential.

That warning given, we get to the good part. One of the most interesting geological surprises produced by lightning is the creation of fulgurites. Fulgurites (named for the Greek word for lightning) are rock formations that often occur when lightning strikes sand and fuses it into the shape of the lightning's path. Most fulgurites are difficult to see against the background of sand from which they were created, twisting and branching like the path of lightning itself. Some fulgurites are formed underground. Because most Florida fulgurites are pretty delicate, treat them gently when you do find them. They crush very easily.

While they are most frequently found in Florida in a wide swath stretching westerly from Cape Canaveral to Tampa, they can be found anywhere that conditions are right, and not only in Florida. Fulgurites have been collected in many parts of the United States, as far north as Minnesota and as far west as deserts in Arizona and New Mexico.

Since you need to know where to find any particular geological specimen you want, a little homework is a good idea. You can start by obtaining various geological maps from the Florida Geological Survey, 903 W. Tennessee, Tallahassee, FL 32304. The cost is nominal. The same material is available with slightly more effort but less cost, from your public library.

Geological map divisions are different from those that are oriented toward agriculture or tourism. Geological maps deal with the structure and locations of various rock structures. William Alexander White, an eminent geologist whose specialties are geomorphology and glacial geology, formulated geomorphic divisions of Florida that make the state's geology much easier to understand.

We will use a general simplified and modified form of Dr. White's divisions here, dividing Florida into the following zones: the Northern Highlands (including the Marianna Lowlands), the Central Highlands, the East and West Coastal Lowlands, and the Southern zone. In the same way that the weather is different from the geographical Northern to Central to Southern zones of the state, so are the geomorphological zones different from one another.

The Northern Highlands stretch across the tops of the most northern counties in Florida. The geology of those counties, and parts of counties, that lie in these Northern Highlands bears a much closer resemblance to that of the counties in Alabama and Georgia which they border than to the rest of the state of Florida. Even the vegetation of the Northern Highlands bears a resemblance to neighboring border growth, from pine forests to the blue-purple glory of wisteria and wildflowers.

Because the Northern Highlands present many treasures unique to that area, in Chapter 3 we will examine the geological conditions that produced those treasures.

Cupped almost in the middle of the Northern Highlands are the Marianna Lowlands, which include caves and many other fascinating features. Fossils are abundant. Some are quite exotic, among them a variety of shells often filled with beautiful calcite crystals, and crystal-lined vugs. A vug is a cavity or hollow in a rock. In Jackson County there are many vugs lined with honey-colored calcite crystals.

When you reach the center point of the Florida peninsula, you will find the Central Highlands. The Central Highlands extend down the center of the state like a long broad finger pointing to the Southern zone and stopping just a little short of touching it.

Along the west side of Florida, the Gulf of Mexico side, lie the West Coastal Lowlands which begin with the southern half of Escambia County and continue along the southern half of the Panhandle all the way down to the Southern zone.

Along the east side of Florida, the East Coastal Lowlands begin at the border with Georgia and follow the Atlantic Ocean south to the Southern zone.

In this book we will pay special attention to sites that you can reach fairly easily and that will most likely be rewarding when you get there. But most of all, we will try to build an acquaintance with enough of Florida's geological features to help you locate for yourself some of Florida's rock and mineral treasures.

A delicate fossil, astrocyclina. A dime is shown as a reference for size.
(Thomas M. Scott)

We will emphasize at this time, and repeat again as we continue, that collecting isn't something you can put off until a more convenient time. Florida is changing so rapidly that a site from which you collected a week ago might be a parking lot next week.

Chapter 2

COLLECTING AND THEN IDENTIFYING

YOU MAY have a fantasy picture of yourself trotting off down the road for home with a huge sack of geological treasures on your back. Nothing wrong with that—as long as it remains a fantasy. Rocks are heavy. You may not get that huge sack all the way home. A successful day of rock hunting begins with planning. Lots of planning.

Think about where you are going. What do you expect to find? And what will you need to take with you to best collect what you do find? Those are the first considerations.

The next is also important: train yourself to calculate weight. Since you will have to carry all of your equipment in addition to your finds, you need to consider how much weight that total will amount to. The prime rule for estimating weight is simple. What you think you must have will weigh at least twice as much in an hour as it did when you started out. You can count on that. The solution is also simple. You carry half as much as you think you will need without leaving behind necessary stuff. Face the fact that the lighter you travel, the more energy you will be able to conserve for actual rockhounding and for carrying rocks.

Whether or not you're a very experienced rockhound, certain equipment is basic. Start with the following essential items:

◆ GEOLOGIST'S HAMMER. The best hammer is sturdy with a special flat head on one end and a tapered pick on the other. (A plasterer's hammer could do instead.) Good quality equipment really counts here. Whatever you carry has to be able to do the job.

Geologist Anthony Gricius wears a hard hat when he searches for crystals in a mine. (Dan Behnke)

◆ CHISELS. You will need cold chisels in two sizes for chipping out small specimens. A one-half inch and a one-inch chisel will give you versatility at the job.

◆ POCKET KNIFE. You might need a knife for a hardness test, as well as for countless other general knife uses.

◆ SAFETY GLASSES. Don't save space at the expense of a pair of safety glasses, which should be worn whenever you do any chipping.

◆ STEEL MEASURING TAPE. It gives you accurate outcrop measurements.

◆ MAGNIFYING GLASS. You need two sizes, 10x and 30x. Many good things come in very small packages. Minerals such as zircon, staurolite, and ilmenite are plentiful in exceedingly small bits in Florida. Because of the ample supply and the greater ease of collecting and storing, many collectors have even begun to specialize in microscopic material. A handful of empty plastic medicine bottles, lightweight and easy to carry, will protect tiny delicate crystals scooped up from drifts of sand and clay. A small, inexpensive hand-held 30x microscope will give you startling glimpses of shapes not generally seen with the naked eye. A microscope like this, or a 10x or 30x magnifying glass, will help you sort out your finds and perhaps discard material you don't want to bother taking along with you.

◆ HEAVY GLOVES and a knapsack with a stout carrying strap.

◆ COMPASS AND PEDOMETER. Getting lost in strange territory can be unpleasant: learn to use your compass before you leave on a rockhounding trip. Careful notations in your notebook about directions help you relocate a good site on a future trip. For the same reason, a pedometer is useful. A pedometer is light in weight and easy to carry and use. It will help you calculate distances as you search out collecting sites and will give you a frame of reference to use in the future along with your compass directions.

◆ MATERIAL FOR WRAPPING FINDS. Newspapers are cheap and useful for sturdy specimens. A handful of fitted-closure plastic bags and a few empty small plastic pill-bottles are excellent for protecting small delicate pieces and for keeping loose grainy specimens separate and safe. If you blow air into a plastic bag that contains a specimen, the air will cushion and help to shield a delicate crystal or special specimen.

◆ CAMERA. Consider seriously the advantages of carrying along a small lightweight camera. It can give you a collection of images of geological material you'd have a very hard time carrying in your knapsack. And a zoom lens can bring in specimens that might otherwise be too difficult or dangerous to approach closely. A camera can provide you with a colorful graphic record for your collection and with material for presentation to interested audiences later on. A camera may be able to gain you entry where a hammer and chisel could not. Sometimes you won't be able to get permission to gather actual specimens, especially if earlier visitors have abused their privileges by destructive behavior. When sites are on private property or on property owned by corporations, you must have permission to gather material—often, even to set foot on the property. It is a lot easier to get permission when you are only asking to take pictures.

◆ NOTEBOOK and several medium-size pencils. Keep these in a pocket or knapsack, convenient to your use. You'll want to write down details of distance and other location notes and a description of the geological setting in which you found your specimens. Your compass and pedometer will come in handy as you map and mark in locations on your collecting map. If your specimens are good enough or plentiful enough, you'll want to come back.

A companion once asked me why I always recommend pencils rather than pens. A few hours later we were caught in a sudden Florida afternoon downpour that soaked us and our gear. Even our notebooks were limp and wet. The pencil marks survived, but notations in ink would have run and probably washed away.

You may want to sketch your specimens and describe their appearance in your notebook so that many weary and confusing hours later you will be able to identify them among others crowding your knapsack. Most important, you will know where you found the specimen. If you ever attend a swap-or-sell gathering of fellow rockhounds, you will discover that being able to identify the exact location where the specimen was found will make a great deal of difference in its value.

When you add fossil hunting to your search you add a whole extra dimension of interest—and gear. The preparations you make to collect and handle your specimens after you find them will be modified, as will methods of preservation and exhibition. Because many sites offer opportunities to collect fossils as well as rocks and minerals, you should be equipped to take advantage of these opportunities. Here are a few additions to your gear that will come in handy:

◆ A couple of small soft brushes
◆ A small whisk broom
◆ An awl and a dental pick

Again, planning ahead is a matter of extreme importance. Carrying home a fossil like a major bone of a mammoth requires specialized equipment and probably a fair supply of manpower, depending on where you find the fossil. But a tiny fossilized shell will require no more than fingers or a tweezers, a pill bottle to protect it, and a pocket.

If you intend to hunt for some of the larger fossil specimens that abound in Florida, you will want to study various excellent handbooks that give you specific suggestions on how to transport specimens safely, how to preserve fossils, and how to display them most effectively. Specialized books on fossils give you specialized instructions for cleaning. Some tell you how to make plaster casts and protective splints for your finds. All show you ways to make the most of the history written in stone that you carry away with you. In the Appendix you will find a list of excellent books about fossils.

A fine place to buy a variety of books on fossils to add to your permanent library is the Department of Natural Sciences and the Department of Paleontology at Florida State Museum, University of Florida, Gainesville, FL 32611. A good reference is M. C. Thomas's *Fossil Vertebrates*. This slim, well-illustrated paperback contains valuable information for the amateur collector. Another good reference for your library is *Fossils,* by William Matthews. More detailed, it contains short historical and biographical sketches and fine clear scientific expositions. Many other good fossil books are listed in the Appendix at the back of this book.

You should also have *The DNR List of Publications* issued by the Florida Department of Natural Resources, Division of Resource Management, Florida Geological Survey, 903 W. Tennessee Street, Tallahassee, FL 32304.

Duane Turner shares his most recent fossil find with classmates at his elementary school. (Iris Comfort)

This fine publication is a treasure trove of valuable information and is moderately priced. It is included in your list of field equipment because the publications listed may be useful to tuck in your knapsack.

Students using library research material should be aware that at various times in the state's history, the Florida Geological Survey has also been known as the Bureau of Geology and the Division of Geology.

◆ TOPOGRAPHICAL MAPS of Florida. These maps are issued by the U.S. Geological Survey, Eastern Division and they are very helpful in analyzing terrain for the best hunting sites. The lay of the land gives you clues for what lies both on the land and under it.

Telephone a toll-free number—(800) 872-6277—to request that an index of maps for the state of Florida be sent to you, along with a catalog so you can order your choice. You will be talking to the Earth Science Information Center of the United States Geological Survey. From these publications you will be able to identify and select maps for your area of interest. Since these maps come in different scales, you can specify which scale you want to use.

Your order will go to:
U.S.G.S. Distribution Center
Box 25286
Denver, CO 80225

You can write to:
Earth Science Information Center
United States Geological Survey
119 National Center
Reston, VA 22092

Property rights of various kinds are an extremely important matter for rockhounds. The dictionary uses words like "formal consent" and "allowing" and "tolerate" and "authorize" but the reality of property rights goes beyond definitions. The reality involves emotionally charged situations when a property owner defends his turf, and it involves legally dangerous situations when an owner defends his rights by calling in police or taking a trespasser to court. It seldom happens but a little information can protect you.

Permission to collect in certain public areas is a very serious matter, with penalties, fines and even imprisonment for violations. Collecting of rocks, fossils, or other objects in national and state parks is prohibited. This prohibition also applies to many county and city parks and lands. Be sure to find out what the rules are for any site that interests you.

If you are interested in collecting fossils, it is a good idea to study a copy of the latest Florida statute regarding fossil collecting. You will find the full text of the 1997 statute at the back of this book. But time passes and statutes change. To get a copy of the latest statutes regarding this topic call the State Legislature Information Division at (800) 342-1827.

The statute was passed in 1993 by the Florida legislature to protect the legacy of the state's vertebrate paleontological sites. The statute specifies that state-owned or -leased lands as well as designated paleontology sites, whether on dry land or submerged areas, are protected by law. Protection is extended to include bones, teeth, natural casts, molds, impressions, and other remains of prehistoric fauna. Mining and quarry and heavy-equipment operators are encouraged to cooperate with the state in preserving its vertebrate paleontological heritage by notifying the Florida Museum of Natural History when such fossils are discovered during mining or digging operations, and allowing access to the experts.

Permission to collect vertebrate fossils on specific sites on state-owned land may be obtained by applying for a permit in writing and by complying with certain conditions. For information on how to go about this, write to:

Program of Vertebrate Paleontology
Florida Museum of Natural History
University of Florida
Gainesville, FL 32611

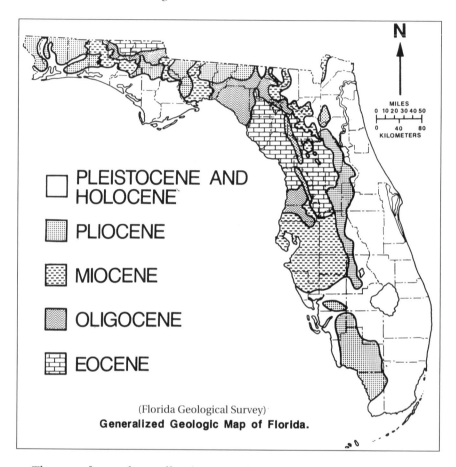

(Florida Geological Survey)
Generalized Geologic Map of Florida.

The cost for such a collecting permit is nominal and amateurs may apply.

If you want to collect in such places as abandoned mine areas, manufacturing sites, tailings, slag dumps and so forth, you will never err if you ask permission. By having gotten permission to look for rocks and minerals, you can assure yourself a welcome back by your care in digging and filling holes, in responsibly driving and parking any vehicles you bring in, and in using care when you open and close gates.

Professional geologists and collectors in the state are finding a growing number of operators whose mines are not open for public collecting. This condition is attributed to owner concerns about safety as well as vandalism. Many rock and mineral clubs continue to be granted access for collecting, however. You might find it very much worth your while to join a collecting organization—a list of some of the clubs in Florida appears in the Appendix to this book—to exchange information, for camaraderie, and for a better chance of gaining access to desirable sites.

Caves also are protected by law in Florida, and there are penalties for violations. The statutes concerning this aspect of Florida caves will be found in the Appendix.

Besides asking for permission to access private property, you can take advantage of a public-relations tool called a *release form*. Property owners are often concerned about accidents or injuries that might subject them to suits for damages. Therefore, I suggest that you create a simple document releasing the property owner from liability for damage to your own property (things like cameras, geological equipment, vehicles, etc.) as well as for injury you might suffer while on the property. You will also state that you will respect the property owner's rights by not interfering with animals and by keeping away from machinery and work or danger zones whether or not they are posted.

Sign each release at the time you present it. Include your address and telephone number if it is requested by the property owner or authorized representative. Photocopying a packet of these releases and observing what they promise will open a few doors otherwise closed to you.

Will this signing off for the owner's responsibility make a great deal of difference? In bottom-line legal terms, no. However it might make a psychological or public relations difference. The property owner knows as well as you do that, given the right circumstances, you could sue for injuries suffered whether you signed a piece of paper in advance or not. But the paper tells the owner that you are careful, responsible, and aware of the owner's needs.

TESTS

There are many tests you will want to make on specimens you gather on a rock hunt. Some of these tests you can make in the field with very simple equipment. Other tests are best saved for your home base where you keep your more expensive and sophisticated equipment. You'll find some of each type below.

More than a hundred years ago, a famous German professor of mineralogy, Friedrich Mohs, invented the test named for him which compares the hardness of minerals. He selected ten common minerals with different hardness and arranged them in order from soft talc at 1 to hard diamond at 10. His rating is still used for rough estimates of hardness, although precise methods of measuring require laboratory equipment.

The Mohs scale of hardness is:
1. Talc
2. Selenite (gypsum)

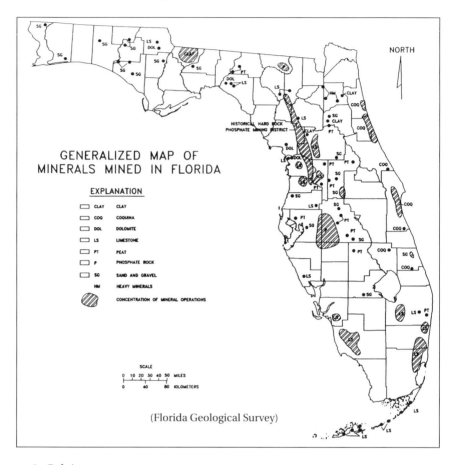

GENERALIZED MAP OF
MINERALS MINED IN FLORIDA

EXPLANATION

☐ CLAY	CLAY	
☐ COQ	COQUINA	
☐ DOL	DOLOMITE	
☐ LS	LIMESTONE	
☐ PT	PEAT	
☐ P	PHOSPHATE ROCK	
☐ SG	SAND AND GRAVEL	
HM	HEAVY MINERALS	
▨	CONCENTRATION OF MINERAL OPERATIONS	

NORTH

HISTORICAL HARD ROCK
PHOSPHATE MINING DISTRICT

SCALE

0 10 20 30 40 50 MILES

0   40   80 KILOMETERS

(Florida Geological Survey)

3. Calcite
4. Fluorite
5. Apatite
6. Feldspar
7. Quartz
8. Topaz
9. Corundum
10. Diamond

Many of the minerals Professor Mohs mentions are not found in Florida or are found in a different form. In Florida you will find examples of hardness for all except the last three numbers: 8. Topaz, 9. Corundum, and 10. Diamond. Florida quartz, rated 7, is plentiful, but as a sand. A common Florida mineral with a 7 hardness is chert.

Gypsum crystals in Florida (number 2 on the Mohs scale) are usually fairly small and very rare. You will find calcite (number 3 on the Mohs scale) in many forms in Florida. If you really look you can find delicate calcite crystals. Any crystal can be damaged by a hardness test, but gypsum and calcite are so relatively soft that no crystals of either one should ever be tested for hardness. Certainly any nice crystal should never be deliberately scratched.

◆ HARDNESS TEST. Basic hardness tests can be done in the field with simple equipment. Your fingernail will test for minerals with a hardness up to 2.5. A penny will serve for a hardness of close to 3.5. If you can't scratch a mineral with your fingernail but you can scratch it with a penny, the mineral has a hardness number between 2.5 and 3.5. If you can't scratch a mineral with a penny but you can scratch it with a knife blade, the mineral has a hardness number between 3.5 and 5.5. A steel file scratches 6.5 minerals. Minerals with a hardness number of 7 through 10 will scratch glass.

◆ STREAK TEST. This needs only a piece of unglazed tile on which your mineral specimen can be rubbed, leaving a trail of powdered minerals behind. Many minerals share the same surface color but have a different-colored streak. Other minerals have quite different surface colors but leave the same colored streak. You will need to know both surface color and streak color to classify your rock.

◆ FRACTURE TESTS. Most minerals break irregularly in a different way one from another. This is called fracture. Three of the most common types of fracture are *conchoidal* (rather like sea shells); *uneven* (which has some angular chunks on its surface; and *earthy* (which looks like a broken piece of earth). Most of these tests are pretty easily managed in the field, but the results are better organized and catalogued at base. When you tackle minerals that split cleanly along certain lines called cleavage planes, you will do better in a workshop setup where you can hold the specimen in a vise and control the force and direction of your efforts.

◆ SPECIFIC GRAVITY TESTS compare the weight of a mineral with the weight of an equal volume of water. A test like this requires a balance scale and a container of water in which to weigh your specimen. This, of course, is best done back at your base.

◆ ULTRAVIOLET LIGHT TESTS. Some minerals absorb ultraviolet light and emit rays of longer length which are apparent to you as colors. There are few fluorescent minerals in Florida. Florida calcite is not known to fluoresce very well but a few specimens do fluoresce. Some rocks continue to show light after the ultraviolet light is gone—a phosphorescent effect. Many variables produce fluorescence in rocks—impurities and their concentration as well as locations. You must test your specimens to be sure that the particular rock you found actually is fluorescent. You can carry a portable quartz lamp for this purpose in the field. Many collectors display their fluorescent minerals in cases illuminated with a quartz lamp to excite the minerals. Argon light produces longer ultraviolet rays.

◆ MAGNETISM TESTS can be made on some Florida minerals, magnetite being one of them. Ilmenite is naturally magnetic but the magnetic property can be increased greatly by heating it. Like any magnet, such magnetic minerals will attract iron filings.

◆ RADIATION TESTS are definitely a specialized activity. Geiger counters must be handled carefully and knowledgeably and in accordance with instructions. Another instrument that detects radioactivity is a scintillometer.

The source of Florida's uranium is the vast resource of phosphate rock in which uranium content generally increases with the content of phosphate, especially marine phosphate. Phosphate is distributed throughout the Hawthorn Group, which covers roughly three-quarters of the state. Other formations, such as the hardrock phosphate of the Ocala Uplift, the Alachua Formation, and the Bone Valley Member of the Peace River Formation of the Hawthorn Group, also contain commercially usable deposits. The formations offering phosphate occur in large areas of the Northern Highlands and the Central Highlands as well as both coastal areas.

Chapter 3

NORTHERN HIGHLANDS ZONE

T HE COUNTIES of the Northern Highlands Zone share Florida's Alabama-Georgia border. Maps you find at the beginning of various zone chapters in this book can help you plan your collecting excursions. You'll have a better idea of what you might find along the way with maps that illustrate where each of the various physiological zones of Florida occur.

The difference between the geological boundaries and the geographical outlines of each county means that this must be considered in planning a rockhound trip. One county may offer an amazing variety of specimens for your collection, depending on where you travel.

Some of the most venerable rock in northern Florida, Paleozoic Erathem in origin, 600 to 225 million years old, is buried so deep only drilling cores can bring it up to the surface. On top of this Paleozoic rock, millions of years of deposits accumulated: the Mesozoic Erathem, 225 to 70 million years old, and over the Mesozoic rock, the much younger rocks of the Cenozoic Erathem, from 70 million years to the present.

Unless you see deep well samples, you will encounter no igneous or metamorphic rock as you prospect in Florida for rocks for your collection. Surface rock is sedimentary.

The map of exposed rocks in Florida in Chapter Two gave you a clearer idea of how, where, and when the rocks you will encounter in Florida were formed. Over much of the Florida Panhandle—that western extension from the top of the peninsula—a Pliocene layer formed.

During a period that extended from 180 million years ago, Florida was submerged. The limestone and dolomite formations of Florida were created from the enormous accumulation of shells and skeletons of sea creatures that were cemented together and compressed during that period. More marine deposits continued to be laid down as sea levels rose and fell during the Miocene Epoch.

Fossils of creatures alive at this time can be found not only in the north central Panhandle, but all over the state—bryozoans, corals, echinoids, and fish bones. Eroding rock deposits from the Appalachian mountains, sands and gravels, began to collect—sometimes in layers, sometimes in pockets—along with the gathering bones and shells.

Fuller's earth deposits (commonly called attapulgite in the Southeast and a term presently being replaced by palygorskite) is a material you might want for a collection of industrial minerals. Palygorskite deposits were developed during the Miocene epoch. In Hawthorn and Alum Bluff sediments of that time you may find mollusks and teeth of rays, sharks, and dugong (sea cows), as well as other marine fossils.

A fabulous assortment of land animals also migrated to Florida as far south as Polk County in this epoch, during times when dry land emerged. The marvelous fossils and minerals you can find in Polk County will be explored in Chapter 10.

Twenty-three counties, either whole or in part, comprise the area usually referred to as the Northern Highlands. The highest point in the state, with an elevation of 345 feet, is located south of Lakewood and east of Paxton in Walton County.

Listing the twenty-three counties from west to east, and keeping in mind that in some cases only a very small portion of the county named is part of the Northern Highlands, there are Escambia, Santa Rosa, Okaloosa, Walton, Holmes, Washington, Jackson, the very northern tip of Calhoun, Gadsden, Liberty, Leon, Jefferson, Madison, Suwannee, and Lafayette counties. The Northern Highlands continue east through Hamilton, Columbia, Baker, Bradford, Union, Alachua and part of Clay and Putnam counties.

In Washington County you can find some nice cream-colored calcite and an abundant selection of marine fossils is available throughout the county. A railroad cut south of Chipley Air Station is a very good place to look.

About a mile beyond the Falling Waters Recreational Area, also south of Chipley, on SR 77, collectors can pick up attractive pale blue chert along the road, as well as in vugs and veins.

Falling Waters Recreational Area offers several geological treats. Falling Waters Hill has two interesting features at its base: an unsuccessful oil

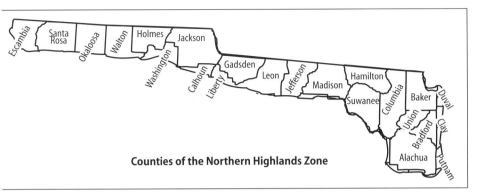

Counties of the Northern Highlands Zone

well that was drilled to a depth of 4,912 feet and a really spectacular sink with a stream that cascades down into its depths. Underlying the area is Suwannee Limestone, overlain by the Chattahoochee Formation with outcrops showing marine fossil shells such as pectens and oysters. Over this lies an Alum Bluff Group siltstone.

This is Karst terrain, an irregular limestone region pocked with many sinkholes and caves. Many cave entrances are located near the sink. There is an 80-foot-high cylindrical dome in Falling Waters Cave. However, this cave is off-limits unless you are an experienced spelunker and have permission to enter from the Florida Park Service.

Common chert is available throughout Washington County as is a good quality flint. The study of chert and flint with their practical applications dates back to the earliest Native Americans. Artifacts show that chert and flint were used by these societies for arrowheads, tools, and other useful implements that might require sharp edges. Because chert fractures in sharp conchoidal edges, it is ideal for such purposes. It is, in fact, so ideal that you might best use a little caution when you grasp a fractured specimen. A friend of mine lifted such a rock carelessly and cut himself painfully in the process.

Although chert and flint have different names, they share a basic commonality. Their big difference is a matter of maturity. Flint occurs when silicification produces a very, very small grain size with highly convoluted boundaries. Light enters these surfaces but does not reflect back out—which gives the rock an almost black appearance. Chert has surfaces with more planes, which not only allow light to come in, but also to reflect back out again. This gives chert a light color.

Knapping is the name for a process used by Native Americans to chip flint and chert to a sharp edge with small scallops, a characteristic of conchoidal fracture. You can find many of these artifacts in all parts of Florida.

Fossil plant frond collected near Alum Bluff. (Thomas M. Scott)

Recognizing the fracture will help you to identify them.

Flint arrowheads may change when they have been buried in Florida soil. Sometimes the darker colored flint changes to the more planed material of chert and develops a sort of rind on the outside. There are two types of rind, one of which is silica from reprecipitation and the other simply grain boundaries straightening out.

Many collectors have made a hobby of knapping flint and chert, fashioning arrowheads and knives and other tools in the style of ancient artisans. Local gem and mineral societies usually know of such activities in their areas and you can check with them if you are interested. You will find a listing of gem and mineral societies in the back of this book.

Around the Chipley area you can find brown transparent calcite crystals, sometimes in clusters and often in inch-long stellate form. "Stellate" describes the star-shaped rays, in this case calcite, which extend out from small centers, delicate and beautiful. While some of these calcite crystals can be found on top of the ground, the stellate types are usually located in less-traveled places like ravines, gullies, and ditches where they are not

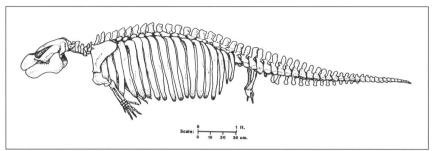

Miocene dugong [Hesperosiren cratagensis] *found in the Floridin Co. Quincy Mine in 1929.*
(Florida Geological Survey)

so easily found. Treat them gently. They are extremely fragile.

Adjacent to Washington County, Jackson County on the Georgia border also offers an attractive chert for collectors: a red chert in which fossils can be found. You can pick this chert up along streambeds in the Cottonwood area.

In Jackson County, check out the limestone quarries. Honey-colored calcite crystals glitter along the fossil shells, often filling cavities. The limestone itself offers a splendid variety of marine fossils, and there is always the chance of coming upon crystal-lined vugs. In the Marianna area the limestone, besides offering fossils, also is of a quality that collectors can polish.

The sediments that form the Northern Highlands are very young (Pliocene) and lie on Miocene rocks. Everywhere you can find young rock laden with fossils.

Gadsden County has some interesting offerings. One of them is commercially valuable fuller's earth. Fuller's earth, a fine-grained, oily feeling clay substance more correctly called attapulgite or palygorskite, has been known for centuries for "fulling." Fulling refers to an earth that can remove grease and oil. In modern times it has served to filter and remove color in the refining of oils and fats.

The discovery of deposits of fuller's earth near Quincy in Gadsden County was important, although many of these mines have been abandoned in recent years as more efficient clays were developed for industrial uses. Silicified trees and vertebrate fossils have been reported as rare finds from these mines. Safety precautions are a must here and so are permissions, but the results are well worth going to some trouble to achieve.

Several mines dealing in all kinds of clay are operating in Gadsden County, two in Quincy. The others are listed by survey references of locales in *The Industrial Minerals Industry Directory of Florida,* compiled by Steven M. Spencer and published by the Florida Geological Survey (see

Attapulgite (fuller's earth) mine near Quincy. What appears as a lighter-shaded roadbed is actually the attapulgite that is being extracted. (Thomas M. Scott)

bibliography). Several sand, gravel, and fill mines also operate in Gadsden County, one in Chattahoochee. The others are listed by survey references with offices in Tallahassee and Chattahoochee. These mines also are listed in the *Industrial Minerals Industry Directory*.

The Apalachicola River runs from Lake Seminole just north of Chattahoochee in Gadsden County to Apalachicola Bay on the Gulf of Mexico, approximately 103 miles. High on its banks you will find Alum Bluff, the state's largest geological exposure and a geological showcase in Florida. Fossiliferous beds from the Alum Bluff Group, the Hawthorn Group, and the Jackson Bluff Formation are exposed on the face of the bluff. Pleistocene terrace deposits are also exposed.

The Bluffs and Ravines Preserve, of which Alum Bluff is a part, is a Nature Conservancy purchase. A map is available and there are good photo opportunities at the bluff overlook and along miles of trail. This particular site can be reached by exiting I-10 (exit 25) at SR 12 and driving about 20 miles southwest. When you reach Garden of Eden Road just north of Bristol, turn right. For further information write: Nature Conservancy, P.O. Box 789, Bristol, FL 32321.

Abandoned mines are fine sources for both vertebrate and invertebrate fossils in the area around Hinson near the Georgia border. You can find ivory in these mines, most often black, and petrified wood, too. Don't omit

Calcite crystals that grew in a vug. (Ken Campbell)

a search of mine dump material. Good specimens can be found there. Again, get permission to enter private property.

Fuller's earth mines in the Jamieson area are also good hunting sites for a variety of fossils, shells, bones, ivory, and petrified wood.

The famous Quincy mines are located about eight miles north of Quincy on SR 65. Explore east of the highway in this area for numerous and varied vertebrate and invertebrate fossils, shells, ivory, and bones. The same good selection of fossils is available in the Havana area off US 27 south of Hinson.

A few counties to the east lies Hamilton County, which also borders Georgia. In Hamilton County you will find an abundance of fossil sites, especially on a stretch of 15 miles upstream on both banks of the Suwannee River from White Springs. In fact, any site around White Springs is excellent.

Hamilton County is located in both the Northern and Central zones. Because most of the county is located in the Central Zone, it will be covered in more detail in Chapter 9.

Holmes County has working sand, gravel, and fill mines in Carryville. Leon has several in the Tallahassee area. Limestone is mined near two Washington County locations: Chiefland and Bonifay. Peat is mined in Madison County, Greenville. When you are in the vicinity of any mine, ask if you may look around and gather specimens. Some important finds have been made that way, especially in fossiliferous areas.

Some very famous and important rivers are located in the Panhandle, and each has its own possibilities for you. The Chipola River cuts through the Miocene sediments of the Chipola Formation, and outcrops offer you corals and shells. Flowing into the Chipola is Tenmile Creek, also laden with a variety of shells and a few vertebrate fossils. Both rivers are spring-fed and very beautiful.

The southern part of Jefferson County has huge deposits of Suwannee limestone, and respectable quantities of dolomite may be found along the Aucilla River. Mammoth and mastodon fossils have been found here, souvenirs from Pleistocene herds. A variety of bones and teeth can be gathered from the river. Also, the very beautiful Wacissa River offers its own share of desirable and plentiful fossils including aquatic rodents. The Wacissa cuts north and south through Jefferson County and joins the Aucilla in the coastal zone of the county. Crossing from one geological division to another within a county can often present you with a surprise quite different from the associated minerals in that county.

Plenty of Pleistocene fossils also can be found along the Steinhatchee and Wacasassa Rivers. Taylor and Dixie are two coastal counties that share the Steinhatchee. The Wacasassa, a short river that empties into the Gulf of Mexico, is in Levy County.

The waters of the Panhandle rivers sing many ballads, about the feathered flocks of birds that left their bones along the Steinhatchee, about the trumpeting voices of elephants along the Aucilla, and of hunts carried on by Indians dead many thousands of years past.

Chapter 4

MARIANNA LOWLANDS ZONE

LIKE A RECTANGULAR-cut treasure box set down mid-way along the scarp lines of northern Florida, the Marianna Lowlands offer a unique rock hunting experience in Florida. Most of the Lowlands lie in Jackson County, covering all of the county except for the southwest corner. But a small western corner of Holmes County and a small northern bit of Washington County are also part of the Lowlands.

Many streams, present and past, as well as many cavern systems in the limestone rock structure, have sculpted this extremely interesting area. The Marianna Limestone Formation in northern Walton County around Alaqua offers a wide selection of fossil shells and marine vertebrates.

Near the town of Marianna, located on US 90, are many limestone quarries where you can find stone of good quality containing fossils.

About three miles north of the town of Marianna, on SR 167, you will find a fascinating introduction to the limestone offerings of the Lowlands. Florida Caverns, glimmering and alive with reflecting calcite crystal, its lowest depth only 65 feet below the surface, is the jewel of this limestone treasure trove. A developed cave, it has a broad selection of amenities, safe access and passages and planned surprises.

Many limestone cavern systems lie beneath the gently hilly woods and farms of the lowlands. There are many picturesque valleys scattered about, left behind by active streams that have cut their way through the ridges and scarps of Alabama and Georgia north of the Florida border.

Limestone is found in almost every state, actually, but the four major cavern regions located in the United States occupy a relatively limited area. Florida is part of one of these four major areas. Caves like those found in northern Florida and its Panhandle area form a slender Y-shaped parade into the south of Alabama, up across central Georgia, with a tip into South Carolina. (The other three major cave areas are located in: 1. A large area extending from northern Arkansas into southern Missouri. 2. A scattered relatively small group in northern Alabama,

Tennessee, southern Illinois and Indiana, Kentucky and the border shared by West Virginia and Virginia. 3. The largest of the major cave areas is found in New Mexico and Texas.)

Karst development has been at least as important to landscape development as streams. Florida has extensive karst plains, sinkholes, and caves. The name came to us from Yugoslavia's Karst District, near the eastern shore of the Adriatic Sea. The limestone rocks there are honeycombed by tunnels and caverns, so most of the drainage is underground. Large sinkholes appear and streams often disappear down swallow holes. These geomorphic features are so characteristic of the Yugoslavian district that the name karst terrain has been applied to any terrain that has been shaped by dissolution of the underlying carbonate rocks.

You may wonder why so many North Central States—North and South Dakota, and most of Michigan, Minnesota, Montana, Nebraska and Wisconsin—have so few caves. Most of those states have large underlying limestone beds so you might expect more cave activity.

Few caves formed in the states mentioned because four glaciers, the last as recently as 8,000 years ago, interfered. These glaciers left accumulated thick layers of debris, gravel, clay and sand called *till* that measured from a few hundred feet to more than a 1,000-feet-deep cushion in some places. In places where the glacial till is relatively thin, however, sinkholes and cracks have appeared.

Two things are necessary to create karst terrain: carbonate rock and slightly acidic water to attack them. Florida has an abundance of both, which has helped it achieve its extensive karst plains.

Many rivers festoon the Lowlands like watery shiny ribbons, the Choctawhatchee, the Apalachicola, the Chipola, and the Chattahoochee.

One of these, the Chipola River, earns special notice inside the boundaries of the Florida Caverns park itself. It disappears into the ground at one point and then, several hundred feet farther downstream it reappears, creating by this action a natural bridge.

The Chipola River offers outcrops of fine shells and corals south of Marianna but the yield is just as good in other places along the Chipola. Try searching the waters to the north of Florida Caverns State Park using snorkel equipment. Pockets of a variety of fossil vertebrates are there to be found. This river offers abundant reward for your efforts, in Jackson County as well as southward into Calhoun County. A canoe is a very good transportation to sites difficult to explore wading. When the river is more clear in the fall months, a canoe offers you access to treasure you wouldn't spot otherwise.

FLORIDA CAVERNS

The Florida Caverns are interesting historically as well as geologically. They lie beneath the 1,783 acres of the Florida Caverns State Park and are part of a network of limestone caves. Dr. Walter Schmidt, State Geologist and Chief of the Florida Geological Survey, provides material from a translation of an account written 296 years ago by a Spaniard, Friar Barreda:

"On June 12, (1693) we continued northwest and after we had journeyed a little more than three leagues, we reached an abandoned village of the Choctaw tribe called San Nicholas where I came to preach the holy gospel in the year 1674. Here we spent the night in the hollow of such a beautiful and unusual rock that I can state positively that more than 200 men could be lodged most comfortably in it. Inside there is a brook which gushes from the living rock."

Archeological evidence indicates that long before Friar Barreda visited the Florida Caverns, hunting parties of Indians sheltered in the caves. Pre-Columbian shards of Indian pottery, ashes from fires, arrowheads, and animal bones bear mute witness to the ancient visitors. More recently, in 1818 a band of native Americans escaped Andrew Jackson's pursuit by hiding in the caves. And during the Civil War, Florida Caverns became a civilian refuge during a military battle.

Florida Caverns are unique among the more than 375 dry caves found in Florida, because the air-filled cave system presents exceptional displays of cave formations. The caverns were formed from Late Eocene Ocala Limestone by the repeated barrage of acidic groundwater and air exposure.

A dazzling array of formations decorates the passages of the Florida Caverns: stalactites and stalagmites, flowstone, rimstone, and a forest of columns that formed when stalactites met stalagmites. Florida Caverns were opened to the public in 1942. Miles of electrical wiring have transformed cave blackness into skillfully lighted dramatic safety.

You won't be able to gather samples of the variety of stalagmites and stalactites festooning the interior of the caverns. Not even small broken fragments may be collected because all material is protected by the state and no collecting is allowed. But you can and certainly ought to take advantage of the opportunity to photograph these particular caverns. Some of your photos may be very special.

Cave bats live in the dark depths of the Florida Caverns, as do ghostly white crayfish and salamanders, both of which have no eyes. Cave bats, here in Florida Caverns as well as any other cave they may call home, are especially vulnerable to visitors. Many people do not realize that bats hibernate and that they should not be disturbed during that period. Many thousands of young bats die each year because people wake them up as they hang upside down, sound asleep, from the ceilings of their underground homes.

Because the water level in the Florida Caverns varies, depending on surface rainfall as well as flood conditions occurring elsewhere, this cave has been developed on two levels. The lower level responds to flood conditions by accumulating water. The upper level is always dry. These varying water level conditions have made necessary the building of several entrances. The choice of entrance depends on the depth and location of water.

Guided walking tours through the Florida Caverns are available. They leave usually on an hourly schedule offered through the Florida Park Service for a moderate fee. The most recent detailed information is available to you by writing Florida Caverns State Park, 2731 Caverns Road, Marianna, FL 32446. It is a good idea to confirm information on the caverns because circumstances may cause scheduling changes. For instance, for several years three-hour spelunking tours were conducted by reservations through parts of the cave not included in the public tour. Many current guidebooks include a listing of the spelunking tours with itinerary, time schedules, and required equipment and physical condition.

These tours have been discontinued at the time of this writing because cave life has suffered damage from the activity. This ecological condition is assumed to be temporary and the tours are expected to be resumed at some time in the future.

Some sources claim the state park contains more than twenty-three caves, an irrelevant speculation. Only the main cave is open to the general public at the present time. If you are a qualified caver, however, you might want to check further.

Like so many natural wonders, the Florida Caverns require a certain

Entrance to the Florida Caverns. (Florida Caverns State Park)

expenditure of time, money, and energy to reach—you don't want to be disappointed in some special feature because you lack informed preparation. The Florida Caverns State Park itself offers full-service camp facilities, both RV sites and camp sites, located near warm Blue Hole Spring. You can encounter an astonishing diversity of botanical growth, and nature trails will take you close to many interesting geological examples—flood plain, Chipola river rise, and limestone exposures, for example. Because it is a developed cave and part of Florida Caverns State Park, it also has a broad selection of amenities.

Swimming, scuba and snorkeling are available and canoes can be rented. Lodging and on-site dive shops are not part of its conveniences. Still, with a little planning and camping gear, you could use the Park as a base and range outside its boundaries to check out convenient collecting sites in the area.

Nearby Blue Springs Recreational Area, also a state park, is located on SR 167. It also offers swimming, scuba, snorkeling and food is available there. Because it is also a state park, collecting is not allowed.

GENERAL CAVE NOTES

Florida Caverns are only one of many caverns that honeycomb limestone in Florida. Approximately 95% of the world's caves are estimated to be found in limestone and Florida's caves generally are no exception to that figure. However, the caverns in this part of Florida are only some of a variety of cave types scattered around the state. Florida Speleological Society files list at least 66 caves above the water level in Jackson county, the second highest total in the state. Information about specific cave sites is an FSS responsibility in Florida to safeguard the safety of cavers with various levels of experience as well as to protect the integrity of the caves themselves.

Whether a cave is wild or developed or totally commercial, if it is wet or dry or a combination of the two, any cave should be approached with caution and respect. The same applies to springs, regardless of where they occur and what your purpose may be in approaching them.

These watery repositories offer special challenge and require a great deal of intensive training for a diver. A snorkeler can get by with good equipment and an adequate guidebook—if he exercises caution, stays alert to hazards, and follows safety rules. But a SCUBA diver must have training. Optimism and energy do not substitute for training and prudence. SCUBA diving can and does turn deadly suddenly. The collecting rewards abound. So do the risks.

Where diving is a major activity in a locale, you will have little difficulty in finding stores that sell supplies for divers. At the back of this book you will find a list of the state parks that have dive shops, as well as information on other dive shops and canoe rental facilities which service river adventurers.

Certain other caves and sinks will be discussed in the zones in which they occur. But a few general cautions are in order here regarding basic equipment and safety procedures for exploring any but commercially developed caves like Florida Caverns.

An undeveloped cave may be called a "wild cave" by spelunkers. As a responsible caver you start a caving adventure by getting permission to enter the cave, of course. If your interest extends to collecting cave material, you also must get permission to collect. Undeveloped caves can be found in many other parts of the state as well as in the Marianna Low-

Speleothems, mostly stalagmites and stalactites, decorate a room in Florida Caverns. (Florida Caverns State Park)

lands. These undeveloped caves are often located near developed caves.

The NSS News 1997 directory lists four active grottoes:
Central Florida Cavers, c/o Avra Thomas
8 Orange Blossom Trail, Yalaha, FL 34797

Flint River Grotto, c/o Aughey
1600 Pullen Road #1-D
Tallahassee, FL 32303-3646

Florida Speleological Society
PO Box 12581, University Station
Gainesville, FL 32604-0581
(J. Johnson; B. Oldacre)

Tampa Bay Area Grotto c/o Mike Kettles
9197 79th Ave N.
Largo, FL 33777

OBTAINING SPECIFIC CAVE INFORMATION

Specific cave diving information is available from officers of the National Association of Cave Diving (NACD) and from the Cave Diving Section of the National Speleological Society (NSS/CDS). Both organizations were formed to train and protect divers as well as to safeguard the fragile environment of caves and caverns and springs. For that reason, both the NACD and NSS/CDS have developed courses of procedures critical to safe diving and the requirements are strict but manageable. Suitable caves and springs matched to your ability will not be too difficult for you to locate.

You might begin by writing or telephoning the National Association of Cave Diving (Florida), Contact person: Dr. Milledge Murphey, P.O. Box 14492, Gainesville, FL 32604-2492; or The National Speleological Society, Contact person: Dave Luckins, 2813 Cave Avenue, Huntsville, AL 35810-4431. Inquire about membership and/or contact with other cavers in the area in which you are interested. Local rock and mineral societies and paleontological societies can also be very helpful. (See Appendix.) Naturally, membership in NSS and NSS/CDS or NACD will give you a head start in training and use of equipment, but people are very good about lending a hand so don't hesitate to ask for help.

CAVE RULES

Regardless of whether you are inexperienced or experienced, spelunking in undeveloped caves can be extremely hazardous. The following rules are absolute musts:

1. Do **NOT** enter any cave alone! A beginner should explore with a companion who is experienced, not another novice like himself.

2. Report to someone on the surface the time you plan to leave to go into a cave and tell them how long you expect to be down there. Be sure they will notify search authorities if you are unreasonably overdue. If no one is in attendance, leave a written message anchored outside the cave entrance with your name written clearly and the name, addresses and telephone number of persons to notify in case you do not return by the time you say.

3. Wear sensible clothing and carry sensible equipment. Caves are dirty and have rock surfaces that are hard and sharp. Crawl spaces and passages may be tight fits. Old blue jeans with a sleeved jacket or heavy shirt offer protection for your hide, and sturdy boots with rough soles give you reliable footing. Smooth-soled shoes will be too slippery to be safe. Heavy gloves protect your hands as you reach for handholds or gather sharp specimens. Wear a hard hat to protect your head from falling rocks or misgauged movements.

A park guide tells visitors cave secrets. (Florida Caverns State Park)

4. Light is so essential in the pitch dark underground world of a cave that each person should carry three different kinds of light in case one or more might fail. In a dry cave carry candles with a waterproof sealed container of matches, a carbide lamp with extra carbide and water, a flashlight with extra batteries. Working in wet caves, springs and other locations requiring diving will demand different and very specialized equipment. Details for wet cave exploring will be given separately.

5. Carry a canteen of water and some small packets of high-energy food. **DO NOT DRINK CAVE WATER EVEN IF YOU FIND IT AS A RUNNING STREAM.** Impurities can seep down into a cave from a variety of sources on the surface: carelessly disposed of industrial waste, animal excrement, decomposing animal remains, and even septic tank drainage.

6. If that underground stream you must not drink from suddenly begins to rise, cut short your visit immediately! Head for the surface, but do not rush carelessly. A wet, slippery, uneven surface along with panic leave you open for accident.

Underwater caves, sinks, and freshwater springs are particularly plentiful in the central and northern parts of the state, though not limited to these areas. Some of them are located in state and national parks, open to the public; some are located on private property. Because Jackson County

Stalagmites grouped like a welcoming committee at Florida Caverns. (Florida Caverns State Park)

has so many such underwater lures, you need to know several vital things before you consider tackling cave diving.

TIPS THAT MIGHT SAVE YOUR LIFE

The first thing you need to do is contact people at the office of the National Association of Cave Diving (NACD) or the Cave Diving Section of the National Speleological Society (NSS/CDS). The second thing is to enroll in the first class available locally, operated by accredited instructors, for your level of expertise. Even expert divers have died exploring Florida's underwater caves, so don't assume your swimming ability and your experience in salt-water diving will protect you. Fresh-water diving is entirely different from salt water diving, in terms of buoyancy and in use of your air-supply.

You'll be taught how to handle an unwinding reel of safety line with a team—your guide to retracing your way. You'll be taught how to handle your air supply so when one third is used your group exits with two-thirds safety margin to go. Some of the deepest caves in the western half of the world are in Florida—your diving limit is a depth of 130 feet unless you are part of a project equipped with special scientific gear.

Three levels of instruction and training are available to prepare you: Spring Diver, Cavern Diver, Cave Diver. How far you want to go with your training depends on just how proficient you want to be. For most collecting, a Spring Diving certification is a solid base. You will be able to use the diving equipment required to explore springs and sinks safely without underwater lights. Natural daylight will give you plenty of illumination for prospecting.

A final safety rule, the same one that applies to any foray below earth's surface, dry or wet: don't go alone. And be sure to let other people know your plans and when you expect to return to base.

The underground watery world of Jackson County offers an introduction to realms fascinatingly different from the sunlit forests and roads and urban growths on the surface. Jackson county has a number of caves and springs sprinkled throughout its karst underworld. One of them, Blue Spring, is a first magnitude artesian spring, bursting up from the Florida aquifer. A list of springs would include Black Spring, Blue Spring, and Blue Hole Spring, Bosel Spring, Daniel Springs, Double Spring, Gadsden Spring and Hays Spring, Mill Pond Spring, Springboard Spring and Sand Bag Spring, and Waddells Mill Pond Spring. There will be more of springs in Chapter 5.

Of the above, Blue Hole Spring is also listed among the state's caves. Caves listed for Jackson County include China Cave, Crotalus Cave, Dynamite Cave, Gerard's Cave (Sam Smither Cave), Honeycomb Hill Cave, Indian Cave, Judge Cave, Justa Cave, London Sewers (The Ovens), Melvin's Cave, Miller's Cave (Pottery Cave), Milton's Cave, Okeefenokee Cave (Water Cave), Old Indian Cave. Rebecca's Hole, River Cave (Devil's Ovens), Soda Straw Cave, Treasure Cave, Washed-Out Cave. The very names of some of these caves and springs hold a lure for divers. The reality often offers high adventure.

Chapter 5

SPECIAL HUNTING TERRITORY
CAVES, SPRINGS, RIVERS, SINKS

WELCOME to more of the murmuring world of rivers, and to that of springs, and wet caves, sinks and caverns! There are troglodyte treasures lying under the winding streams and swirling waters! Some geological collectibles in Florida come with enough extra excitement to turn rockhounding into grand adventure. Your introduction to Florida State Park Caverns in Chapter 4, along with some of the rivers and springs and caves and sinks of Jackson county, was only the beginning.

This chapter will go into additional detail about exploring caves and collecting from rivers and certain springs. You will find more specific instructions and tips on this sort of collecting here than in other chapters. Some rivers wander great distances in their journey across Florida and you will find them in several different geological locations, so many rivers will be included in more than one chapter.

Florida has 34 major rivers. We'll check out some good collecting sites in several of them in this chapter. Many of these rivers "braid" at channels—the Aucilla, for instance. Creeks and streams branch off others, offering an abundance of fossils. If you have time, it will be well worth your efforts to explore such waters for collectibles. Canoes and boats can be rented along many rivers and scuba gear is available for rental at most spring and cave diving sites.

Rivers, whether large or small, come with a variety of temperaments, as do springs and caves. Some rivers sprawl down across the Alabama and Georgia borders into north Florida, across the Panhandle and into the Gulf of Mexico. Many rivers spawn springs, or slip into subterranean caverns; most carry fossils, artifacts, and other interesting material in their waters. There are very few places where you can't find something for your collection.

CAVES

Caves, more than 375 of them—and speleologists consider that definitely a very modest estimate—offer adventurous experiences as well as photographic opportunities. There are caves where you rappel sharply down into the earth and others where you squirm into coral that gives you only 3 feet of clearance. Some caves are dry caves, some are huge subterranean underwater caverns that extend for many miles under such a teeming city as Tampa. Depths may range from less than 20 feet to 5280 feet. Cave lengths may range from less than 20 feet to systems of more than 30 miles. While some caves are dry and some wet, some are a combination of the two.

Entrances to caves also vary, from horizontal to vertical, from highly visible to almost concealed. In some cases you enter from a pit or chimney, in others by a spring or a sink, even from a mine or a quarry.

Take and Leave Nothing But Your Footsteps. From some caves an owner might let you gather a stray fossil or artifact. Unless you have express permission, you may take nothing.

It is expected that cavers do not disturb or willfully damage speleothems or carry them off to display in collections, and responsible cavers don't. Which is why, of course, you can still find caves with beauty to admire. The code is to leave a cave itself in the condition in which you find it, and to leave nothing behind but your footprints.

There are severe penalties for infractions and we repeat: laws protect Florida's state and federal parks and caves and regulate collecting in caves. So you must secure any needed permissions in advance. Instructions for applying for such permissions are in the Appendix. Permission to enter caves as well as other property when private owners are involved is a legal necessity as well, in addition to permission to collect.

The National Speleological Society pays $250 to $1000 for any information leading to the conviction of anyone who violates state or federal laws protecting caves. This offer, established in 1981, also applies to gates and other devices protecting caves. A recent issue of National Speleology's *News* reported 35 convictions of cave vandals from 1981 to 1997.

Vandalism and accidents, many fatal, have scared various landowners into denying access to good caves by any but authorized qualified cavers, or cavers with previous access.

Tampa Bay agatized coral found near Tarpon Springs, just south of Tampa on the Gulf of Mexico. From the Jack Cummings collection. (Michael Smith)

Unexpected cave treasures may sometimes become available to you. Often, very shallow caves contain exquisite calcite and other crystals, exposed in the course of a commercial mining operation. You won't find such caves named or listed as locales for your prospecting. They usually don't last long enough to list if the company is hunting for other raw material. But I have seen some excellent specimens taken with permission from these shallow caves.

WET CAVES, SPRINGS AND SINKS

Wet caves, springs, sinks—the whole panoply of underwater wonders—present a totally different challenge. Despite the beguiling rewards of the underwater world, no prudent speleologist forgets for a moment that this is also a dangerous unforgiving world. This is a realm of dark rushing waters, springs that burst to the surface, of currents that may swirl silt in clouds. Silt can blind an unwary diver and disorient him. There simply is no safe room for error. Springs and caverns demand special skills and safeguards, but once you learn the drill you can have a terrific time.

Use of new sophisticated equipment has given divers access to more underwater cave networks than ever before, but this very access has cost even expert divers their lives. Several experienced scuba divers met disaster in Florida caves for a tragically simple reason: they came from a vacation of diving in the Caribbean Islands and neglected to allow for the critical difference between fresh water and salt water characteristics when they changed venue.

Another pair of certified cave divers braved a central Florida cave in July when summer algae bloom resulted in extremely poor visibility. One of the divers, only recently certified, became lost. Three days later searchers recovered his body. Still relatively inexperienced, he had become trapped in a situation he was not yet equipped to handle.

Another hazard for divers is not life-threatening but it is startling and unpleasant: a two-inch-long tadpole called a madtom. It's a member of the catfish family and it has sharp venomous spines that can deliver an extremely painful sting. This is a creature best avoided.

If you build experience conservatively and don't overreach your capabilities, you will be able to enjoy cave and spring and sink diving safely. Attention to detail and moderation is a good modus operandi.

RIVERS

Rivers in Florida have formed a strange fantastic bridge from prehistoric times to the present, because of their changing existences and courses.

Some of the cool whispering waters over which we'll suggest that you paddle your canoe in search of fossils were once nothing but gathering clouds overhead and gathering spring water deep in the aquifer. In Pleistocene times tapirs roamed a grassy plane that nurtured a wide variety of creatures. The marvelous bones of these and other long extinct animals pass below your canoe like shadows from a time-warp waiting to be discovered. Once you identify your finds and research the creatures from which they came you may discover a whole new dimension to the river sliding by, exciting time-overlays that turn backward and forward literally in the blink of your eyes.

The AUCILLA RIVER seeps into Florida from Georgia and follows an eccentric course south through the Panhandle, passing 40 miles east of Tallahassee. It forms a boundary between Jefferson and Madison counties for some miles, then, downstream it forms a boundary between Jefferson and Taylor counties. Elephant fossils are famous finds here. In 1997 Dr. E. David Webb's underwater archeology team working at 30 feet found the bones of camels, giant sloths, jaguars, prehistoric llamas, and tapirs as well as around 36 other extinct animal fossils. This site is believed to be that of Paleo Indians who were mammoth hunters. Volunteers come for two months each summer and fall to work at the site.

A canoe is good equipment for prospecting on the Aucilla. Snorkeling will help you find material in deep holes as the river snakes along. Check the shallows and rocky areas. Keep your eyes open for bones and teeth. There are lots of them and you can come upon them unexpectedly. Innumerable sinks, most often water-filled, are good hunting grounds.

ABOVE: *These turtle shell pieces represent a variety of species. They are taken from the Withlacoochee River, but are common to all Florida rivers.*
RIGHT: *Lower jaw bones with four molars from a horse* (equus). *Found in the Withlacoochee River. From the collection of Jack Cummings.* (Michael Smith photos)

Five miles of the Aucilla flow underground, hidden from view except for dark deep sinks that mark its course like strewn cosmic bread crumbs. Risky stretches of rapids and a few man-made dams do not give you un-limited access by canoe so inquire before you start a trip. A good place to prospect is south of LAMONT, a town located on the junction of highways US 27 and CR 257 in Jefferson County. At the east edge of Lamont you can put a canoe afloat, access on US 27. You will find plenty of good material in rocky shallows and along the north bank in the stretch between Lamont and the take-out where CR 257 crosses the river once more seven miles south of Lamont.

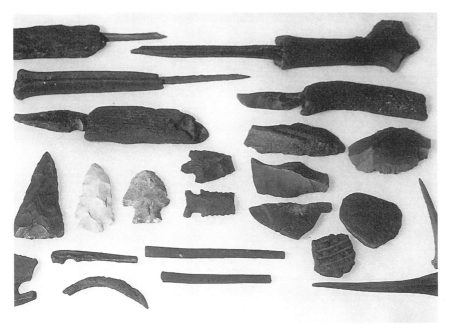

12,000-year-old Indian artifacts found in the Suwanee River at the site of a prehistoric mastodon hunter's camp. From the collection of Jack Cummings. (Michael Smith)

Many other rivers in the Panhandle are good collecting rivers, TENMILE CREEK in Calhoun County, the Wacissa in Jefferson County. Downstream from WACISSA SPRINGS on the WACISSA RIVER lie about 14 miles of vigorous canoeing to US 98, a 14 miles of paddling studded with a dozen natural springs. Try scuba gear in the largest, BIG BLUE SPRING, close to 50 feet deep.

The watery crooked finger of the SANTA FE RIVER divides Columbia County to the north, from Gilchrist and Alachua counties to the south. You'll find lots of shark and manatee teeth in the Santa Fe and scuba and snorkel gear will offer you good choice among other fossils that have settled into many deep holes along the river. Easy access to the river is available from SR 47 near Fort White and from US 27.

The WITHLACOOCHIE RIVER, or Crooked River as named by the Indians, is one of five important rivers that owe their existence to the GREEN SWAMP, an 870 square mile area that supplies 70 percent of the water Florida uses. The other rivers are the HILLSBOROUGH, KISSIMMEE, OKLAWAHA, and PEACE. Cities on the boundary of the swamp are Clermont (just a little north of the beginning of the Withlacoochie, Brooksville (Hernando County), Zephyrhills (Pasco County), Haines City and Lakeland (both in Polk County) and Clermont (Lake County). Back in Pleistocene times this whole area was alive with terrestrial animals long extinct. This is a fine place to collect

The core of a large piece of rare chalcedony material that was percussion flaked with a hammer stone by prehistoric Indians. The pieces were used to make knives, or converted into arrowheads by pressure flaking. The characteristic conchoidal fracture of this material made it ideal for use as edged tools. This core was uncovered in the Withlacoochee River near Yankeetown. From the collection of Jack Cummings. (Michael Smith)

fossil bones, both older marine fossils as well as terrestrial. Prospecting on land sites will be found in following chapters in this book.

The Withlacoochie River is a fascinating treasure chest whether you search the waters in Polk County or follow its twisting course all the way to Withlacoochie Bay, which empties into the Gulf of Mexico up in Citrus County near Yankeetown. People have found good collectibles in a stretch between the SR 44 bridge and the SR 200 bridge. You'll also find ramps for canoe access.

Echinoids and sand dollars are abundant on the river bottom near Yankeetown. Other larger bones are taken along the Withlacoochie: peccary; dermal plates from edontates such as glyptodont and armadillo; jaws and teeth from little pleistocene horses; tapir; large ground sloth teeth and more. Diligence will net you big rewards.

The Peace River squiggles its way through De Soto and Hardee counties. The name of the Peace River has a long history: called *Rio de la Paz* (river of peace) by the Spanish, it was later the peace boundary during the Seminole wars. Its 130 miles, from near Bartow in Polk County to the Gulf of Mexico, offer a tremendous amount of fine fossil material, Miocene to Pleistocene. A good place to rent a canoe is the Canoe Outpost in Arcadia.

From October through July, the Peace is shallow and you can find great hunting along the river's edges in the gravel and sand. Carry a screen and wash out teeth and bones. Like the Withlacoochie, this is a river that was frequented by many animals and you can find imposing large mammoth bones as well as big mammoth teeth. Dugong ribs are very common. Snorkel is a good choice of equipment to use here, especially during the shallow October through July period. HORSE CREEK, a creek near Arcadia, also yields plenty of fossils. Snorkel is a good choice for this water, too.

Some rivers need lots of room. The SUWANNEE RIVER is one of them. Its leisurely powerful loops swing down from OKEFENOKEE SWAMP in Georgia, through Hamilton County and between a series of counties, until some 235 miles later it ends at the Gulf of Mexico in its namesake village, Suwannee. The Suwannee makes its way down the Northern Highlands Zone south, slowly continues its way, touching Madison County on one side for a while, Suwannee County on the other. Farther south it murmurs its way into the Gulf Coastal Lowlands Zone, lapping Lafayette and Dixie counties, Gilchrist and Levy counties. Chapters 3 and 6 offer additional information for collecting geological specimens in the Suwannee area.

More than 80 springs merge into the Suwannee. Some of them are very dangerous so be sure to plan ahead and inquire about the particular spring that interests you.

COLLECTING

Keep in mind that few waters offer the range of interesting collectibles as the romantic historic Suwannee. Artifacts as well as fossils are abundant. The artifacts shown in this chapter are from the collection of Jack Cummings, an Orlando collector. They illustrate some of the fascinating material other people have found in this river. This material was located on the bottom of the Suwannee at the site of an ancient mastodon hunter's camp, and dated approximately 12,000 years ago, when land rose dry and clear where the river now flows.

A variety of tools and weapons are shown in this chapter. The rows display flint stone knives and bone awls, each item with its original bone handle. Arrowheads, chert as well as flint, were also found at this site, as were the sharp edged scraper knives and cutting blades.

From shark tooth to mold frame to plaster cast: Charles Howlett shows his method for duplicating collectibles. (Michael Smith)

HOW TO DUPLICATE ITEMS YOU COLLECT

You will need:
◆ A small amount of scrap wood and a saw to cut it to the sizes you select for the frame to accommodate your specimen.
◆ A board to back the frame. Nail it securely to the frame.
◆ Liquid latex and a paintbrush.
◆ 15 squares of cheesecloth, cut to the size of the backing board.
◆ Plaster of Paris, water, and a container for mixing.
1. Paint each piece of cheesecloth with latex and layer the pieces in the bottom of the box formed by the frame and backing board.
2. Set the specimen on top of the last layer of cheesecloth; press down firmly. Then coat the specimen with latex. Let it all dry in place.
3. When the latex has dried, mix the plaster of Paris with water to a heavy cream consistency and pour it into the wooden box. Let it dry .
4. When the plaster is dry, gently remove the specimen (as in the photograph). The plaster itself can then be used as a fine mold, viz:
5. Oil the plaster mold and fill it again with more plaster to create a plaque. Or, cut away the plaster matrix, leaving a reproduction of only the specimen, which you could then paint to resemble the original.

Natural molds are sometimes found in fossiliferous limestone; you can use them to make plaster casts of the original fossils. Clean out the mold first, then coat it with a light grade of machine oil. Mix plaster of Paris with water, as above, and pour it into the stone mold. When it is dry, remove the plaster cast of the original fossil.

Pockets of fossilized bones and teeth covered by mud are often uncovered by rushing river waters, leaving cleaned bones visible. However, many fine specimens have been recovered by carefully digging them from residual mud and by using swift river currents to wash away accumulations. River waters often cut through sinkholes, exposing prehistoric remains of animals trapped by flood, collapse of domes of ancient caves, or by any number of disasters that froze lives in time. Silt and runoff from surface openings may collect in caves and sinks and these sediments cones almost always contain a variety of fossils. Karst features found throughout North and Central Florida produce many of these cones. One cone located in a cave in Alachua County near Newberry produced a yield of armadillos and tortoises and the fossils of baby mastodons.

Fossils may be collected from some caves but again, you must contact a branch of the Florida Speleological Society first for information and needed permissions and second, to confirm that you are trained in safe caving. What you find in caves is usually of value. Many prehistoric animals denned up in caves and left their bones to accumulate with the marine vertebrates that had left their own bones long before the terrestrials arrived.

Some fossils are well preserved and some require knowledgeable methods of preservation to keep them safe. There are many good paleontology references available to help you deal with a variety of conditions that Florida caves can impose on a collector and to help you identify specimens. The list of books in the Appendix offers you a selection so you will be better equipped to protect your finds. But a quick once-over here will get you started.

PRESERVING

Bones you find in sediments like silt and sand are easily removed and lifted by small tools. The trouble is, they will probably be pretty soft after ages spent in humidity and the effects of soil chemistry. In this case, undercutting and removing matrix or soil along with the fossil will protect it from damage. Later you can clean it up. One of the ways you can harden soft damp bones is to treat them with water based resins. Acrysol is a good one. If you want to remove the resin later, acetone or ethanol will do the job. Butvar 76 or Acryloid B-72 are also good hardeners, but they do best on dried material.

Plaster jacketing is the time-honored process of protecting a difficult specimen. A fast and fancy method for using it is to apply three inch plaster orthopedic rolls (bought at a surgical supply store) and wetting them down, then wrapping your prize. An outer covering of toilet paper or soft toweling will further protect it until the jacket dries. Old-fashioned fast drying plaster of Paris is messier and you'll need to have a pail along for mixing, but it works fine, too, and it's a lot cheaper. Water and wrapping material, burlap or old clean strips of cloth, will give you what you need for a good jacket. Toilet paper or other covering will finish the transportation protection.

Mending may be done with epoxy, if you can make sure the surface involved is both clean and dry. Epoxy should be used on dry days, not in humid weather—and finding a dry day in Florida is a challenge. Follow directions for epoxy use and give it time to cure. Super Glue holds as it absorbs moisture from the air—but additional moisture ruins the bond once it has set up. That makes it a dicey solution for most field problems.

On some excursions you may find very few of a popular specimen. If it happens on a school or Scout field trip this can be a major disappointment.

Charles Howlett, a Central Florida collector solved this problem with a simple reproduction method for making plaster casts, as shown in the photograph and step-by-step sidebar on page 56.

The memorabilia of a prospecting trip can provide exhibitions for classrooms, libraries, museums, as well as personal collections. Multiplying your treasures by making molds and casts gives a special kind of luster to your venture. Photos and handbooks provide additional interest for an exhibit.

ALLIGATORS

Since we've been concentrating on the waterworld, one last denizen needs to be mentioned: alligators. Keep your eyes open and proceed with reasonable caution. We can assume you already know that you must not feed "gators," nor allow children or pets free rein in places where alligators congregate, murky shallows along a river, grassy swampy areas. But there are a few things to remember for yourself and other adults. Keep aware of your surroundings and don't leave the security of a canoe without checking out the water carefully. Alligators are territorial. If you hear their distinctive resonant grunt or you see them cruising around, a prudent retreat is in order. You can always find another good prospecting ground somewhere else.

Chapter 6

GULF COASTAL LOWLANDS ZONE

IN THE FLORIDA PANHANDLE, the beginning of the impressively long Gulf Coastal Lowlands Zone appears much closer geological kin to neighboring Alabama and Georgia than to the rest of Florida. Closer inspection, however, shows that the zone is far more coastal than highland in character.

Even though the Gulf Coastal Lowlands extend all along the Gulf coast from Alabama to the beginning of the Southern Zone, which begins halfway through Lee County, only seven counties are wholly within the Gulf Coastal Zones: Gulf, Franklin, Wakulla, Lafayette, Taylor, Dixie, and Pinellas.

Large areas of the remaining Gulf Coastal counties also lie partly within the Central Highlands Zone: Hamilton, Suwannee, Gilchrist, Levy, Citrus, Hernando, Pasco, Sarasota, Hillsborough, Manatee, Charlotte, Hardee, De Soto, and Glades counties. One coastal county, Lee, shares its area with the Southern Zone. Bay County is partly in the Northern Highlands Zone.

This coastline extends down close to the center of the Florida Platform. The hilly backbone of the state extends from the Georgia-Florida border south to Highlands County. But most of the Florida land area which extends out away from this backbone actually lies on the east side of the center of the platform. Where is the western side of the platform? It's out there, but it's submerged under the waters of the Gulf.

Eocene and Oligocene limestone and dolostones are exposed along the west coast from around Jefferson County on down to Pasco County. You'll find this stone randomly visible in Taylor, Dixie, Levy, Citrus, Hernando, and Pasco counties. Geological material in this area has been significantly altered by the elements. You'll want to keep your eyes open as you drive or hike along the coast here. Exposed rock is common and you can find good specimens for your collection in the altered rock.

Sloping south from the oilfields, piney woods, and farms of the northern portion of the Panhandle counties, each county has an "apron" of coastal geological material extending from its middle down to the Gulf of Mexico. As you look for unique specimens for your collection, the hundred miles of white dazzling quartz sand beaches and bays from Pensacola to Panama City will lure you, and justifiably so. But when you're in the Pensacola area, remember that this colorful city had a flourishing brick-making industry at one time, dating back to the Spanish occupation. Bits of old brick and some of the clay which made them are interesting collectibles for school projects.

The brick making industry, founded on need and the supply of good clay available, continued to grow with changing populations. First the Spanish, then the French, again the Spanish, then the British, the Spanish again and finally the Americans under Andrew Jackson occupied the city. The Confederates seized it during the Civil War but left when Fort Pickens did not fall. A lot of rebuilding went on after each change of occupation. This was a prosperous clay-mining area until the 1960s. You will find records and artifacts of those times in the Historic Pensacola Village in Pensacola.

Steven M. Spencer's "Industrial Mineral Operations in Florida" map for the Florida Geological Survey, available through the Survey, supplies an up-to-date record of mining activities all over the state. Sand, gravel, and fill are the principal mining products for the coastal Panhandle, except for one operation in Gulf County that deals in magnesium and brines.

Deposits of dolomite occur along the Aucilla River at CR 257 in Jefferson County. Several inactive limestone mine sites can be found near the Aucilla about five miles south of the junction of CR 257 and US 27, and also down near US 98.

Pyrite, also called "fool's gold," sometimes occurs in dolomite or dolostone in several deposits in the state. Any pyrite crystals you might find won't be in the form of the showy silver-brassy collectible crystals you might find elsewhere in the United States. The crystals in Florida pyrite are very tiny but they are to be reckoned with. The cement industry, which uses a lot of Florida dolomite, considers the presence of pyrite in dolomite a real pest. Pyrite occurring in concrete will cause costly discoloration because pyrite is an iron sulfide, and like any iron, it will rust.

Limestone is a sedimentary rock, composed mainly of calcite, which is

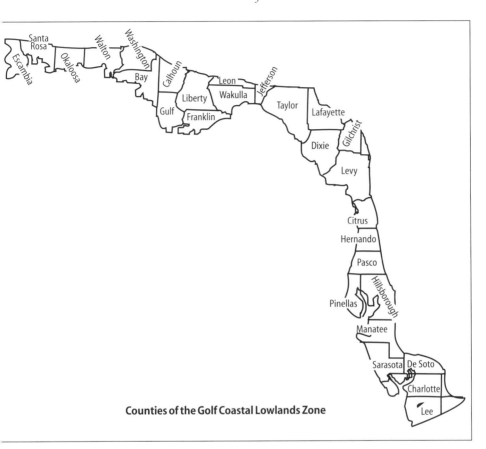

Counties of the Golf Coastal Lowlands Zone

calcium carbonate. Depending upon where you find it in the state, the composition of limestone may vary somewhat. Ocala Limestone underlies most of Florida but surfaces in some counties in the Panhandle, south to Citrus County, and in the Central Highlands.

Ocala limestone is the purest of this rock. In it you may find many desirable fossils. Suwannee limestone is very pure but it is not quite as pure as the Ocala limestone. It has very little clay and quartz. It occurs as far south as Pasco County. Other limestones, oolite in the Southern zone, and limestone mined with other material, will be discussed in other chapters.

The Perry area in Taylor County is a good place to look for fossils. One of my favorite spots is west on US 98 past the Econfina River bridge, then south on SR 14. Near the Econfina are coral and other interesting specimens, but it is privately owned land and you must have permission to look around here.

For collectors, all of Lafayette County has quarries where you can find marine fossils and agatized shells as well as petrified wood. Keep in mind that a working quarry and any posted area is off limits unless you secure permission to prospect.

Moving south along the Gulf Coastal Lowlands Zone, we come to the Levy County border and then to Citrus County. South of the Florida Barge Canal and about a mile south of the Levy-Citrus border on US 19, you will come upon a mine site that is no longer open. You will need permission to prospect around here, even in the spoil piles. The calcite crystals are excellent: the colors of some of them are transparent and bright, in various shades of yellow. There are also white crystals and very good marine fossils. Some fossils are filled with calcite crystals.

Farther south, off US 19/98, you will come to Crystal River. Near the town, on Rock Crusher Road, you will find a huge limestone quarry, now inactive, owned by the GTE Satellite Systems Corporation. Again there are abundant fossils of marine creatures, often filled with calcite and transparent crystals clear and in various shades of yellow. You can find nice chert here, too.

Watch for chert nodules in Citrus County among the excavations and road repairs and the railroad cuts. Also keep your eyes alert for fossils and pieces of ivory. Some of the photographs of calcite specimens appearing in this book were taken at various locations in Citrus County. The area around the town of Lecanto is known for its calcite.

Some calcite crystals here form in the same distinctive way that certain calcite crystals form in South Dakota. These calcite crystals grow in the sand and ultimately retain the shape of the crystal but a matrix that is mostly sand. They are not common, but you can find them in the Crystal River area.

The first thing geologists will talk about when you get to Hernando County is the marvelous calcite to be found in the Brooksville area. The second thing they talk about is the damage irresponsible people have done in the easily accessible caves in the area—speleothems snapped off, names written on the walls, places generally trashed and stripped. Caves are protected by law from vandalism and removal of speleothems now, of course, but damage done in the past takes a long time to live down.

Many great places to hunt for calcite in Hernando County around Brooksville are available to you. Road and railroad cuts offer good hunting to a diligent searcher, and any kind of dredging or construction operation is bound to turn up calcite crystals and marine fossils. Fossils often are filled with calcite crystals.

Dr. Frank Kujawa is a geologist who loves crystals and revels in the outstanding specimens he finds in Hernando County. Particularly he likes

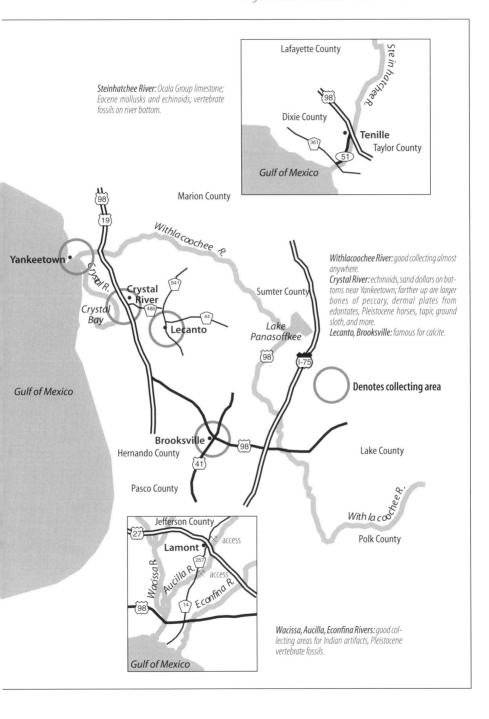

Steinhatchee River: *Ocala Group limestone; Eocene mollusks and echinoids; vertebrate fossils on river bottom.*

Lafayette County

Steinhatchee R.

Dixie County

98

Tenille

361

Taylor County

51

Gulf of Mexico

Marion County

98

19

Withlacoochee R.

Yankeetown

Crystal R.

Crystal River

941

486

Crystal Bay

44

Lecanto

Sumter County

Lake Panasoffkee

Withlacoochee River: *good collecting almost anywhere.*
Crystal River: *echinoids, sand dollars on bottoms near Yankeetown; farther up are larger bones of peccary, dermal plates from edontates, Pleistocene horses, tapir, ground sloth, and more.*
Lecanto, Brooksville: *famous for calcite.*

98

I-75

Denotes collecting area

Gulf of Mexico

Brooksville

98

Hernando County

41

Lake County

Pasco County

With la coochee R.

Jefferson County

27

access

Lamont

257

access

Wacissa R.

Aucilla R.

Econfina R.

98

14

Polk County

Wacissa, Aucilla, Econfina Rivers: *good collecting areas for Indian artifacts, Pleistocene vertebrate fossils.*

Gulf of Mexico

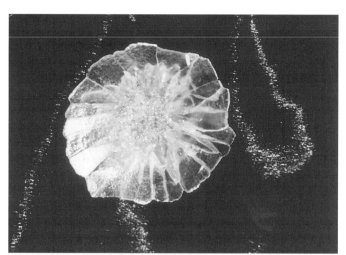

Calcite is found in countless varied forms. Fossils are often filled with calcite crystals. (Thomas M. Scott)

finding well-preserved pieces of limestone where the imprint left behind by a long-dissolved shell has acquired a covering of tiny quartz crystals that give a velvety sparkly surface to the interior. He's found many of these in Brooksville area limestone, as well as calcite crystals, some of which show traces of iron and phosphate iron. Iron in particular tends to stain calcite, changing it from almost colorless to shades of yellow and brown.

A cloudy or opaque calcite crystal, Kujawa says, may be caused by little cracks in the crystal, possibly small bits of clay—something outside the perfect crystal structure that tends to scatter light.

Kujawa is also fascinated by qualities of aragonite occurring in fossil shells. Most collectors are interested in fairly large aragonite crystals, but they are difficult to find and preserve. Most organism-produced minerals like aragonite are considered a high-energy form.

Aragonite, if it is fairly recent or has been protected in some way, may well survive so it can be analyzed, but it is less stable than calcite and it often dissolves preferentially. In many rocks there are spaces where shells have dissolved, while around them other shells remain, preserved because they are calcite. Sometimes you find shells where the aragonite has dissolved and an infilling of a cavity by calcium carbonate has occurred. Or an infilling may consist of microscopic quartz crystals. These quartz crystals would be considered a secondary deposit. Chances are they would be yellowish in color compared to the matrix.

The area around New Port Richey in Pasco County is another fine place to find calcite for your collection. Bailey's Bluff, just west of New Port Richey, is known among collectors as a good place to prospect. Inactive quarries and excavations yield marine fossils filled with calcite crystals. "Tampa Bay agate," a popular name for a beautiful translucent chalcedony in orange, pink, blue, and brown that line some coral geodes, is found here. Watch for finds among repairs that involve digging. Also check construction excavations in Pasco County.

Tarpon Springs and Dunedin in Pinellas County, across Tampa Bay from Hillsborough County, also are fine places to find "Tampa Bay agate." In Dunedin there is good hunting on the tidal flats of Honeymoon Island and along the banks of the Caladesi Causeway as well as on Caladesi Island. Selenite crystals have been found in Gulfport on US 19, but they are not common. Gypsum crystals, most often found at great depths, have also been taken from material dredged up at Gulfport. Pinellas is a coastal county where pearls turn up now and then in the lakes and streams.

A paleontological site that is famous worldwide is the Leisey Shell Pit near Ruskin in southwest Hillsborough County. An extremely able amateur paleontologist named Frank Garcia has made significant finds in the Leisey pit in the past decade. Joined by members from the staff of the Florida State Museum and dedicated groups from various mineral and fossil societies, he sent a huge collection from the Leisey pit to the Florida State Museum to be studied and analyzed. The search continues. In March 1993, Garcia unearthed what he believes is the largest Ice Age sloth claw ever found. A long-haired creature that resembles a bear, this sloth *(Eremotherium)* stood 18 feet tall and weighed about 20,000 pounds. The age of the fossil is estimated to be 1.4 million years.

Many of the geologists in the Tampa area have availed themselves of the work done by dredging operations in Tampa Bay. When a ship channel was dredged, several spoil islands were built, and from the spoils some fine material was picked up. Among the minerals found were barite, calcite, and quartz. In this case it was necessary to use a boat to reach the islands, but the collecting was certainly worth the effort. Good pseudomorphs also were found in McKay Bay near a spot that was being dredged. A pseudomorph or "false form," as its name suggests, is a mineral crystal whose internal structure has been altered although its external form remains the same.

Ballast Point in Tampa has been long famous for the silicified coral heads found there. An interesting story about this site begins when the causeway was started. A developer determined to build condominiums on an island dredged all around it and built a few condominiums off the causeway. But he never did develop the island and finally the state bought the land.

A unique situation developed because of that condominium project gone awry. Parts of the beach became armored with pieces of silicified

Tampa limestone that were dredged up, making it one of Florida's few rocky beaches. Also dredged up were grapefruit-sized balls of agatized coral. These are not museum quality, of course. Some of them are broken open and you can see the coral structure in them.

Fine Ballast Point chalcedony is prized by many collectors. Chalcedony is a fibrous quartz with an interesting formation habit. Quartz crystals require low concentrations of silica in the water and a long time to form. Quartz crystals are not built very easily. If their nucleation rate is very fast or if the silica concentration in water is very high, opal forms. About 120 parts per million silica will make opal. If it's down in the 60s and 70s, the only way silica can coordinate is in needles. And that forms chalcedony. If the concentrations are down to 10, 11, or 12, the nucleation rate is very slow; particles lock in the right way to make quartz crystals. It is a matter of concentration and rate.

There are big deposits of opal in Tampa Bay. There are outcrops in Hamilton County in North Florida and Marion County, and in phosphate mines. Opal is pretty widespread in Florida. Not precious opal, but it is opal.

Coral specimens can also be found at Pioneer Park, a Hardee County park on CR 64A, about five miles south of Wauchula. The 100-acre park is located on Rock Lake. Hardee County is located northeast of Sarasota County.

The riches of Sarasota County—and they are riches—are fossils. You can play at the beach, trying to scoop up fossil shark's teeth from the water or other sea debris with the strainers available at beach supply shops up and down the coast. Some entrepreneurs drive to the Gulf Coast as well as to Polk County to gather bags of fossil shark's teeth to make into jewelry or to sell as curiosities.

Many sites are not procrastination proof. Chairman of the Geology Department of the University of South Florida, Dr. Mark Stewart, told me about a spot near Sarasota, just off US I-75. His description was enticing: a mine with a high section of shell rhizomes, almost 30 feet high, with branching corals and some bone material. Manatee and whale bones were found near the base of this deposit. The deposits were from the Pliocene Epoch, Pinecrest Formation. For years, hundreds, perhaps thousands of people visited that shell pit paying a small fee to dig fossils, partly because it had been so widely publicized.

Unfortunately, if a visit to the Newburn Shell Pit was on your agenda, please be advised that it is no longer doing business. There's not even a telephone number anymore. This is yet another wise reminder to do your homework ahead of time, especially if you are making a long trip for a particular objective and you don't want to be disappointed.

Crystal River Formation rock studded with small shell fossils. A dime is shown for size reference. (Thomas M. Scott)

The shorelines of the Intracoastal Waterway offer fossil surprises along both banks in the Venice area: vertebrate and invertebrate fossils, shells, and lots of shark teeth in very good condition. Bones and teeth of animals you don't ordinarily associate with the Gulf coast bear witness to a teeming ancient animal population. Elephant, camel, sloth, horse—you can find teeth of any of them here.

From Venice Beach south to Charlotte County you can find a still more amazing variety of collectible fossils, especially in the Manasota Key part of the county. Vertebrate and invertebrate fossils abound. You can find teeth from shark, mastodon, horse and sloth. Camel teeth have also been found.

When you reach Charlotte County, check out the Punta Gorda area south along US I-75. You may come upon some unusual calcite: nice crystals, some of which are stellate clusters. And there will be a wide selection of marine fossils, some of them with calcite replacements.

A certain amount of serendipity is involved in rock collecting. Opportunities can be missed if you don't invest time and energy at the right time. An exciting locale that you plan on returning to another day may well be gone a short time later. The dynamics of rapid development in Florida—residential, business, and entertainment—affect all aspects of life in this state.

CHAPTER 7

THE SOUTHERN ZONE

OIL PUMPS nod industriously over their wells in Lee County east of Port Myers. Many more wells work fields in Hendry and Collier counties. Here famous Alligator Alley crosses Big Cypress Swamp and the vast Everglades. Alligator Alley begins just east of Naples and ends at the western fringe of Fort Lauderdale. Everglades National Park stretches its patchwork of water and vegetation and outcrop across the southern tip of the mainland. Bright cities are strung along the eastern coast like glittering subtropical beads.

Seven colorful counties form the southern part of the Southern Zone: Martin, Hendry, Palm Beach, Collier, Broward, Monroe, and Dade. Four more counties lie partially in the Southern Zones: Lee, Glades, St. Lucie, and a very tiny tip of Okeechobee. There's a lot to see in these areas as you go about your collecting activities.

The Southern Zone of Florida has an identity all its own, possibly because it is relatively young and wayward, as geological ages go. The oldest formation is Tamiami limestone—and that is only about 3 to 5 million years old—of the Pliocene epoch. You will find this limestone mostly in the upper western part of the Southern Zone: a patch in eastern Lee County, almost all of Collier County, and a small part of Hendry and Monroe counties.

A little younger, at approximately 2 million years, a drape of Pliocene Caloosahatchee marl settles across the top of the Southern Zone. Marl is a crumbly stratum composed mostly of sand, clay, and calcium carbonate. This material is found in most of Hendry County south of Lake Okeechobee.

The Fort Thompson Formation, layers of marls and limestones and sandstones, began to form in the central part of the Southern Zone more than 100,000 years ago. Around the same time, Key Largo limestone began to form in the keys, and the Anastasia Formation developed in the north on both the western and eastern coasts. Over a large portion of the southern tip of the zone, Miami limestone began its existence in a swirl of seawater and sand and sea creatures.

The Fort Thompson, Key Largo, Anastasia, and Miami Formations all shared approximately the same time frame—the Pleistocene Epoch. The varying conditions under which the rocks in these formations occurred, however, resulted in surprising differences in their characteristics.

Back then the ocean was almost 25 feet higher than it is now. The Ice Age gradually resulted in lower water levels and a great many other geologic changes. Such factors as the formation of oolitic limestone, colonies of bryozoans (also known as "moss animals" because of their appearance), and the changing distribution of sand and weeds played roles in shaping this part of the state.

The periodic invasions of sea and wind and the forces of burgeoning life all contributed their parts to change and development. Many little marine creatures lived and died and left lasting prints behind on the shifting ingredients of the forming land. As part of limestone rock, these creatures are the essence of a multi-million dollar mining resource and a valuable industrial product.

Everglades rocks are a combination of oolitic limestone and enormous dominant colonies of knobby bryozoans, known as *Schizoporrella floridana*. Bryozoan facies of the Miami limestone extend widely through three south Florida counties: Broward, Collier and Dade.

Worm tubes are common in the Everglades. These fossil remains were once used by living creatures that extracted building materials from the water around them. From these materials the marine worms constructed limestone shells and used this armor to protect themselves from predators.

A black fossil horse tooth, lying in the shell bed where it was found. A pocket knife is shown for size reference. (Florida Geological Survey)

Anastasia and Miami formations made their appearance some 100,000 years ago. As the freezing water of the Ice Age in polar regions lowered sea levels, oolites and bryozoans in Florida were no longer covered. This material became land. Eventually this land was cemented together to form hard rock. The rock up around Miami and Homestead, in Dade and Broward counties, illustrates how this process worked.

All across the Southern zone, ranging from the Gulf of Mexico to the Atlantic Ocean, canals now slice into the land. Spoil pile banks alongside the canals await discovery. On the Gulf side, the canals of southern Lee County and western Collier County cut through some fascinating Pliocene patch reefs. As you travel south on CR 951 you can take advantage of spoil piles left along the road and add some good fossils to your collection.

A canal runs the entire length of CR 951. Every half mile or so it passes through one of the little patch reefs where you can find some of the molds formed by shells of oysters, scallops, and other shelled sea creatures in the formerly calcitic mud. When the mud changed, the shells dissolved and imprints or molds of the shells were left behind. This molluscan facies has a molded porosity; when you pick up a piece, you can see molds

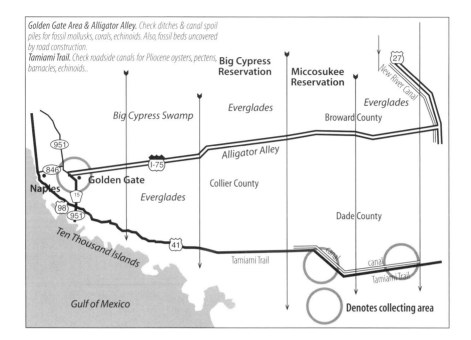

Golden Gate Area & Alligator Alley. *Check ditches & canal spoil piles for fossil mollusks, corals, echinoids. Also, fossil beds uncovered by road construction.*
Tamiami Trail. *Check roadside canals for Pliocene oysters, pectens, barnacles, echinoids..*

Big Cypress Reservation

Miccosukee Reservation

27

New River Canal

Everglades

Everglades

Big Cypress Swamp

Broward County

951

I-75

Alligator Alley

846

Golden Gate

Collier County

Naples

15

Everglades

Dade County

98

951

Ten Thousand Islands

41

Tamiami Trail

canal

canal

Tamiami Trail

Gulf of Mexico

Denotes collecting area

of shells long gone from the scene.

Some calcite finds from Cape Coral in Lee County have coral visible in the calcite. Some of the most beautiful have been collected from a drainage ditch in Cape Coral. Now that same ditch is grassed over in an area filled with houses. The time for finding such crystals easily has gone.

Three limestone areas dot Lee County. The first forms a huge amoeba shape low in the eastern part of the county. The other two smaller areas lie in the northeastern corner. All three areas have both active as well as inactive mines.

A large limestone area, located just south of Lehigh Acres Oil Field and west of West Felda Oil Field, has four mines located along Alico Road. Two inactive mines lie on either side of CR 887 where it intersects Alico Road. Two active mines operate just off Alico Road toward the east from US I-75.

The route from Tampa to Miami on US I-75 (Alligator Alley) across the state will take you past the same kind of Pliocene reefs as you encounter in Lee and Collier counties—and the same easily accessible collecting spots. Spoil piles are surprise packages scattered along canals and excavation sites. There's no way to predict from appearances what you may find. Some treasured geological material has been added to collections by rock hounds who stopped to poke around a likely-looking spoil pile.

Vizcaya Museum and Gardens offers stunning examples of Florida limestone and keystone used architecturally. Florida oolithic limestone is used for the stone brackets under the roof, the quoins at the corners, framing around the windows and doors, and trim lines on the central bay of the façade. (Doris Littlefield)

Crushed stone, oil, and gas are basic commercial minerals of Collier County. The crushed stone comes from open-pit limestone mines; the limestone is from Tamiami Formation, Pliocene Epoch.

Several inactive limestone mines and two active mines are located in western Collier County near the county seat, Naples, off CR 951 between CR 886 and 856. CR 886 is also known as Golden Gate Parkway. CR 856 runs parallel to and two miles south of Golden Gate. It is also known as Radio Road. Other limestone mines are scattered along CR 846 in northern Collier County.

Golden Gate Estates, just east of Naples, is an area Dr. Mark Stewart, Chairman of the Geology Department of the University of South Florida, has always found rewarding. Canals built every quarter mile have resulted in a great many spoil piles from cuts made in Pliocene reefs. Corals and a wide variety of fossil shells can be found in this development, which is about 15 miles long and about six miles across.

Among the fossils you can find without much trouble are fine quality fossil echinoids, which are plentiful in Collier County. Good oolitic limestone is to be found in the southeast part of the county. Oolitic limestone is composed mostly of little spheres of calcium carbonate known as ooids. As always, the spoil piles deposited by canal building invite investigation.

Keystone, quarried at Windley Key, is used for flooring and steps in the arcade at Vizcaya. (Vizcaya Museum & Gardens)

Many oil fields are completely or partially located in the county. A number of wells have been drilled in Corkscrew Field and Lake Trafford Field in the northern area. USGS Well 625-116-1 is also located in this area. Sunniland Field, Pepper Hammock Field, and Baxter Island Field are centrally located, and Racoon Point Field is in the southeast area. Each field contains a number of wells.

South of Collier County you come upon Monroe County and the wonders of Everglades National Park. Even though the law forbids your carrying off any of the geological material you may find in the park, you will revel in the photo opportunities available. If you reach Monroe County by taking US 41 (also known as the Tamiami Trail), you might head south on SR 29 about four miles until you reach the western visitors' entrance on the north side of Everglades City.

A second entry site, the park headquarters, is located about ten miles

Field stones on the high wall are Florida limestone. The obelisk and urns, also of Florida limestone, were made by stonecutters on the site. (Vizcaya Museum & Gardens)

from Florida City. Follow West Palm Drive in Florida City, turn left at Tower Road, and signs will lead you about nine miles to the park entrance.

A third visitors' center is located on US 41 about halfway between the Everglades City ranger station and the main headquarters. This entrance is known as the Shark Valley Visitor Center, and you will find it about 40 miles southwest of Florida City. A fourth Everglades National Park ranger station is located on Key Largo. Any of these centers will supply you with a wide selection of information and printed material to enhance your visit. Park employees are able to direct you to the areas you want to visit.

Earlier in this chapter you read about the limestone found in the Southern area, and some of the particular rock to be found in the Everglades: the oolitic and bryozoan facies.

Remember that while you cannot collect from the Everglades National Park area, the Everglades itself extends far beyond the park boundaries, forming a broad band across the central Southern zone. On the eastern side it reaches a finger as far north as the latitude between Palm Beach and Belle Glade, and it covers large areas of Broward, Dade, and Collier counties as well as a squarish area in the northeast corner of Monroe County. In other words, there is a vast expanse of the Everglades that you *can* explore in a search for rocks unique to this region.

A great deal of mainland Monroe County is occupied by the Everglades

National Park. Actually the Florida Keys constitute the major mass of the county, and Key West is the Monroe county seat.

The keys form an arc that begins in the waters off Miami and curves down to Key West. Divided naturally into two sections, the islands of the upper keys extend to Big Pine Key and are composed of Key Largo limestone. The lower keys, which include Big Pine Key and Key West, are composed of Miami limestone.

Forty-two of the keys are connected by the Overseas Highway. The eastern shores of all of the keys are washed by the Atlantic Ocean, and the western shores are splashed by Florida Bay and the Gulf of Mexico. All of these islands have foundations of 125,000-year-old dead coral reefs. "Dead" is an important distinction, because located here in the same area is a unique living coral reef, the John Pennekamp Coral Reef State Park.

This state park is the only one of its kind in the world and an exciting opportunity to photograph ancient coral and limestone rock structures as well as a modern living counterpart. The living coral and animal communities in the modern reef illustrate how the ancient reefs were built. Adjacent to John Pennekamp Coral Reef State Park is the Key Largo Coral Reef National Marine Sanctuary.

From Soldier Key to Newfoundland Harbor Key in the Upper Keys there are numerous outcrops of Key Largo Limestone. Construction spoil piles also deserve close scrutiny here. Many varied coral fossils, among them brain, porous, and rose coral, are found in this locale. Most of the material is fragmented. Some of the specimens are intact and well worth your time and effort to search out.

The narrow Atlantic coastal ridge of the mainland emphasizes the difference a few feet can make during a hurricane as the ocean rises, surges, floods whatever it can reach. Miami's Coconut Grove has a land elevation of almost 20 feet. Elevation in the Everglades may range from 10 feet above sea level in Broward County to five feet in Monroe County and parts of Dade County. This is a locale where high winds and waters periodically rearrange man-made structures to an unrecognizable degree in just a few hours. It is fascinating to see geological rearrangement done on a much vaster scale by the same elements.

Miami limestone, composed of oolite, is the bedrock underlying the Atlantic coastal ridge. You can see outcrops readily because the soil layer is so thin. But the best places to see how this limestone was layered in is by viewing cuts made for canals and excavations. One famous site is located in Coconut Grove at Silver Bluff. Here the layers of cross-bedded sand and sea creatures rise like a giant elaborate geological layer cake set somewhat askew as a result of careless handling. The oddly angled layers of oolite and sand were laid down, tossed by the sea, settled again, and cemented together by time, pressure and chemical action.

As oolitic rock, oolite is both beautiful and valuable. Quarries scattered where it is available have supplied building material for a large number of structures, some of them apartment buildings and public offices, the most famous being Vizcaya, a Miami showplace.

Calcite crystals can be collected along the southern coast, some of them growing on coral fossils in exotic conformations. One collector found a little coral specimen with calcite growth that looks like a small Chinese god. Many such oddities are available to sharp-eyed hunters. Chalcedony, occurring as a coral replacement, is also to be found in the Miami area; in fact, it is referred to as "Miami agate." Heavy limestone mining continues in the coastal counties, but as you head north, the limestone mining emphasis steadily changes.

Large portions of western Martin and Broward counties have huge peat deposits. Sand, shell, and marl are mined on the eastern portions. The hunting isn't nearly as good on the east coast as it is on the west. But you can add coquina rock, and east coast rock, to your collection. And you can find interesting fossil remains in the limestone: sponge spicules, mollusk fragments, and foraminifers. You can find these fossils, as well as coral and echinoid spines, in the shell marl and clay.

Chapter 8

EASTERN COASTAL
LOWLANDS ZONE

A MAGIC QUALITY surrounds rockhounding in the Eastern Coastal Lowlands Zone, a combination of the sight and salty sea-fragrance of the vast Atlantic and of miles of beach sand, banded intermittently with shaded ribbons of heavy minerals. As you stand on ancient sands that once covered the bottom of a much wider and very deep sea, you might look up to see a rocket arcing off into the blue sky from John F. Kennedy Space Center.

The exposed portions of the Eastern Coastal Lowlands Zone date from the Pleistocene (about 1.8 million to 10,000 years ago) and Holocene Epochs (recent ages, geologically speaking). These formations share the same Pleistocene time frame as some southern Florida rocks.

But one very important fact of temperature made a great deal of difference: the glacial ice mass that periodically approached Florida came much closer to northern than to southern Florida. The spreading glacial ice crept down to within 500 miles of Florida before it stopped.

What did each of the glaciations mean to Florida? During the Pleistocene Epoch, also called the Glacial Epoch or Ice Age, more than one-fourth of the earth's surface was covered by glacial ice mass. Between each of the four Pleistocene glaciations came thaws when the water level rose again, only to fall when a new frozen sea of glacial ice crawled down from the north. Each episode changed the surface of the land: adding, subtracting, altering. The Pleistocene Epoch devoured huge amounts of seawater in its glaciations and each glaciation forced great numbers of

77

animals to flee south for survival.

The fossil remains of various creatures that lived in Florida make this state a wondrous repository of fossil treasure. Many species—saber-toothed tiger, rhinoceros, and camel among them—roamed Florida, then disappeared. But many left behind fossils, teeth, casts, and molds. Bones and teeth fossils are primary remnants of the presence of these creatures; the bonus is the great number of casts and molds.

In Chapter 5 you shared a fellow-collector's method for making his own plaster of Paris casts and molds. Nature's method is not so very different.

A mold is an impression made in surrounding material of an organism pressed into it. In time the organism itself disappears but the trace or impression is preserved by the hardening material. This material formed outside to make exterior molds and inside to make internal molds. A cast occurs when material forms inside a mold and hardens there. Natural molds and casts that preserve traces of such former life are considered fossils. By using such artificial means as plaster of Paris, wax, or liquid rubber, you can make molds and casts yourself of fossils you collect, and share them with fellow collectors.

Fossil remains give us clues about the identity and lives of the creatures. Just as important, their presence in certain rock strata is used to date the strata in which they are found; they are known as guide or index fossils.

All surface rock in Florida is sedimentary and sometimes that surface has surprising accumulated layers and depth. Beneath such accumulated layers, igneous and metamorphic basement rock occurs thousands of feet below the surface. Even professional geologists have only scant information about the deepest locations. This information is always important to you as a collector when you must identify the origin of rocks encountered and recognized as having originated some distance from Florida. They may possibly have been hauled into the state in a commercial load or dropped accidentally.

Some forms of rocks could not possibly have come from Florida, even though the mineral is found in the state. For instance, staurolite. Staurolite occurs in heavy mineral sand and other sands in Florida. But in Florida it does not occur in a monoclinic twinned form familiar to Georgia collectors and jewelers as a cross.

Zircon is found in some Florida coastal areas. But it is found in the form of sand, small grains. Gem-quality big crystals of zircon suitable for jewelry come from other parts of the world. However, the zircon found in Florida is also valuable. Florida is the most important source of zirconium silicate, the chief mineral of which zircon is composed and which is mined by two companies in Clay County.

The Eastern Coastal Lowlands zone begins with the northern half of St. Lucie County. Including St. Lucie County, eight counties have shores scoured by the Atlantic: St. Lucie, Indian River, Brevard, Volusia, Flagler, St. John's, Duval, and Nassau.

The Eastern Coastal zone doesn't consist only of sea-washed counties. A few miles inland, an additional eleven counties are, at least partially, included in the Eastern Coastal Lowlands. The names of some of them may surprise you: most of Glades, Highlands, Okeechobee, about a third of Polk, most of Osceola, Orange, Lake, all of Seminole, a slice of Marion's eastern side, most of Putnam, and Clay.

You were introduced to fulgurites in the first chapter. Although the fused silica forms produced by lightning can be found anywhere in Florida, a very good place to look for fulgurites is on the Atlantic beaches. Dr. Frank Kujawa, a professor at the University of Central Florida, reports finding many fulgurites shaped like nodules on these beaches. My own collection includes a box of fulgurites found in a sand and silica mine site in Polk County.

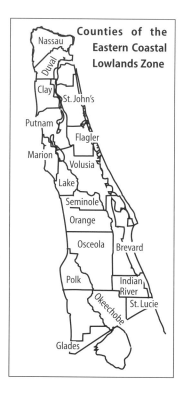

Counties of the Eastern Coastal Lowlands Zone

Charting a route on US 1 will bring you closer to the relatively limited number of places in this zone that offer geological specimens for your collection. As you head north into Indian River County you will pass through Sebastian, where sand and fill are mined.

Heavy minerals have been mined in Indian River County in the Vero Beach area. Where deposits occur of sufficient commercial interest to be mined in an area, you can usually find quite interesting specimens. Look for dark ribbons of black heavy minerals shading off to gray along the beach sands anywhere and scoop some into a pill bottle for your collection. Watch for a sparkle of quartz grains, especially in the lighter mineral. It won't be valuable, but it will be interesting.

Cape Canaveral was the site of important geological studies in the last two decades. The Florida Geological Survey in cooperation with the United States Minerals Management Service, the University of Texas at Austin, the United States Geological Survey, and the University of South Florida teamed up to investigate offshore shoals. Their purpose was to discover

Whale vertebra from a Brevard County shell pit. (Thomas M. Scott)

possible sources for strategic and critical heavy minerals. They found il-menite, rutile, zircon, and monazite. They also reported finding minerals of less economic importance: staurolite, aluminosilicates (sillimanite/kyanite/andalusite), garnet, and phosphate.

Large samplings of sediment gathered from the shoals were processed through a hydrodynamic spiral for this investigation. The sediment was first separated between heavies (concentrate) and lights, then put through a number of complex tests. The results in terms of locating valuable de-posits were commercially disappointing—low potential compared to onshore economic deposits such as Green Cove Springs and Trail Ridge. However, the variety and amount of minerals are still considered an im-portant resource.

Whale vertebrae have been found recently, buried in a shell pit in Brevard County. Other fossils can be found in spoil piles and accumula-tions of shell material in this area.

Limonite can be found in several places along the South Coastal Rail-road line in the far northwest corner of Volusia County. Limonite, also known as bog-iron, is a brown hematite. Here it occurs in the form of yel-low ochre, which is a soft clayey material that was mined during the first half of this century for paint pigment. You can recognize its presence by its characteristic rust stain on surrounding soil or stone.

Coquina is a fossiliferous rock: shells cemented together with calcite. Some of the mollusk shells cemented into this rock have survived intact.

Coquina mined in Flagler County is from the Anastasia Formation,

Castillo de San Marcos, built of coquina rock during the Spanish period between 1672 and 1695. Coquina, relatively soft when cut, hardens with exposure. (National Park Service)

which extends from Anastasia Island in St. John's County south for about 150 miles. Clay deposits are scattered about the county, mostly occurring in many small deposits. Three large deposits are located on the Putnam County boundary, and a fourth, larger deposit, lies about five miles north and slightly northeast.

St. John's County, entirely located within the Eastern Coastal Zone, has many active mines as well as some inactive sites. One active coquina mine is located approximately three miles west of St. Augustine; the other is approximately four miles north and slightly west. Both are situated in a large coquina-rich area ballooning out to the south, west, and north of St. Augustine. Because both mines are active, permission to visit them is necessary. For collecting purposes, any of the coquina areas west of St. Augustine will produce fine specimens for your collection. Another coquina area is located on the ocean at the boundary of St. John's and Flagler counties.

A clay-rich area stretches just south of St. Augustine along the ocean, off SR A1A. Several other clay areas are scattered through the county, but this one is easiest to reach and is representative. If you are including clays in your collection, this area will yield an interesting addition.

Away from the ocean but a coast lowland county truly, in its character, Putnam County has huge sand deposits. Sand mines dot the county, some active, some inactive. In the gray and green sediments of the Hawthorn, you may find fossils of mollusks, shark teeth, diatoms, and foraminifera.

Florida's first heavy-mineral mining was done in Ponte Vedra, which was known at that time as Mineral City. Heavy minerals produced in 1916

A great arched chamber at Castillo de San Marcos shows how well coquina has held up under three centuries of hard use. (National Park Service)

included ilmenite for titanium and tetrachloride. These minerals were used in World War I in the manufacturing of such materiel as tracer bullets, spotting shells, and smoke screens. Other minerals mined in Mineral City included quartz, feldspar, zircon, rutile, monazite, staurolite, epidote, and garnet. One heavy mineral historical site is located in Ponte Vedra, just off SR A1A.

Heavy minerals such as zircon, ilmenite, and rutile are found in the Jacksonville area, Duval County, about five miles east of Interstate 295, near the Ortega River just northeast of Cedar Hills. This is a case where cruising around with your eyes open will net you good material for your collection.

Although you will find information about the more exciting finds of Polk County in Chapter 10, the part of the Polk County that lies in the Eastern Coastal Zone has its share of treasures. Pearls show up occasionally at spots scattered about the county. Drainage ditches are a good place to look. Check out the area near Kathleen ten miles from Lakeland on CR 35; you may be lucky enough to find one in any Polk County lake or river. Excellent fossils in great abundance are found throughout Polk County.

Chapter 9

CENTRAL HIGHLANDS ZONE

T HE FOREFINGER shape of the Central Highlands Zone rests on the backbone of the Florida Platform, from the Georgia border pointing down to the middle of Glades County. Several counties— Hamilton, Columbia, Baker, Suwannee, Union, Bradford, Putnam and Alachua—cluster in an area referred to by many geologists as the Northern Zone of the Central Highlands Zone.

Located partially or wholly within the southern portion of the Central Highlands Zone are Gilchrist, Levy, Marion, Citrus, Sumter, Lake, Orange, Osceola, Hernando, Pasco, Hillsborough, Polk, Hardee, De Soto, and Highland counties. The tip of Glades County near Lake Okeechobee is also included in this zone.

One way or another, you're always conscious of water in Florida. It laps at the peninsula along its more than 1,300 miles of coastline. It comes down from the sky in the form of summer deluges and seasonal hurricanes. It flows in its 34 major rivers and uncounted small ones. It rests in about 7,800 lakes that dot the predominant green of plant life like blue spangles reflecting the beautiful sky.

Many of the rivers and most of the lakes are located in the central part of Florida and most of them are located in Lake, Orange, Osceola, and Polk counties. Of the incredible number of lakes in central Florida, lakes that are not man-made very likely are karst sinkholes that filled with water. One of the ways you can identify them is by their characteristic round shapes.

The exceptions are a few of the larger lakes that geologists theorize originated as sea bottom depressions in the Ice Age. Lakes Okeechobee and Istokpoga as well as some larger lakes in the Kissimmee and St. Johns river valleys are believed to have been formed this way.

Because Florida was nearly covered repeatedly by sea water, countless sea creatures found habitat as waters rose—only to be stranded later as water fell. When the seas receded for the last time, more stranded creatures were left behind. Their bony remains, consisting of shells, the bones of early whales, dolphins, fish, echinoids, foraminifera, and other marine life, were gradually compacted and cemented together.

As happened in the Northern Highlands Zone and the Marianna Lowlands Zone as well as other places with favorable conditions, huge rock formations appeared. Layers formed, composed largely of calcite, aragonite, and dolomite, the building minerals of ancient shells and corals. Karst regions developed.

Carbonate rock, formed by compacted marine remains, responded to attacks of acidic water and became perforated by caves and sinkholes. Some professional geologists estimate two-thirds of the peninsula and the eastern half of the Panhandle to be riddled with sinkholes.

Sinkholes are very much a dynamic fact of life in the Central Highlands Zone. Whether sinkholes date from the Miocene or much more recently— and some are opening up in the earth even as you read this book— sinkholes are very important to collectors. The conditions that create sinkholes are dynamic in nature, governed by change and subject to inexorable physical rules.

You may encounter ancient sinkholes that became repositories for bones of large and small land animals, vertebrate as well as invertebrate. These animals no doubt fled the northern cold and after a time, passed into fossil history. Invaluable fossils, artifacts, and minerals might be preserved under a layer of water or mud until some scientific prospector is perceptive and diligent enough—or fortunate enough, to come upon them. Or you might find a Paleo-Indian artifact. Or the battered remains of a jalopy that plunged to an early sinkhole grave only a decade or two ago.

Rivers are also exciting. The Alapaha River is a particular favorite of Dr. Mark Stewart, Chairman of the Geology Department of the University of South Florida, a collector himself. There are many reasons why this river is special.

The bed of this unusual river, dry most of the year, runs under a bridge at US 1-10 near Live Oak. A great deal of the bed of the Alapaha is limestone, pocked by many sinkholes.

There are gravel bars in the river, made up of fairly coarse sands and

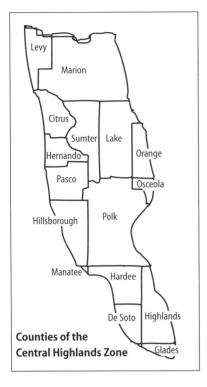

**Counties of the
Central Highlands Zone**

pebbles that come down from the Piedmont in Georgia. Most are made up of limestone chunks and coarse sands with gravel eroded from the Hawthorn Group. That makes them different from anything you might find anywhere else in Florida.

The river rises in Georgia and takes along with it some coastal plain sands which are Piedmont-derived. The water drags this sand into Florida—you can see this sand in the gravel bars alongside the river. You can also find coarse angular sand, heavy gravel, and quartz and other pebbles that have been wrested from metamorphic rocks. But most of the sand is derived locally from the Hawthorn Group and younger units.

North of US 1-10, the Alapaha forms a little flow called Dead Creek Flow and dives down, both river and flow, into a massive sinkhole. For the next 17 miles the river disappears. Suddenly the Alapaha rises at the Suwannee, joining as a powerful, first-magnitude spring known as the Alapaha Rise. The water of this spring is brown and stained with tannic acid. Dr. Stewart describes it as river water that flowed directly under 17 miles of land without mixing much with groundwater. Not only is the water dark and stained with tannic acid when it comes up at the spring, but it is also loaded with suspended material.

No gem-quality specimens appear in this accessible hunting ground, but you can find extremely interesting geological material, particularly if you are interested in fossils.

The Suwannee River loops its way into Hamilton County from its beginning in the Okefenokee Swamp in Georgia. Most of the river is dark with tannin, except for places where springs dilute localized areas. Hamilton County is wonderfully rich in both minerals and fossils, particularly around the White Springs area on the upper Suwannee River. For more than ten miles, on either side of the river, you will be able to find marine fossils and coral heads. You can find very attractive agate in the area near Stephen Foster Memorial, which is on US 41.

Hamilton County has both Ocala and Suwannee limestone. These lime-

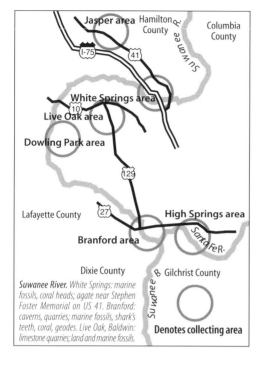

Suwanee River. White Springs: marine fossils, coral heads; agate near Stephen Foster Memorial on US 41. Branford: caverns, quarries; marine fossils, shark's teeth, coral, geodes. Live Oak, Baldwin: limestone quarries; land and marine fossils.

Denotes collecting area

stones are richly fossiliferous and contain bryozoan, mollusks, foraminifera, and echinoids.

Several major springs are located in Hamilton County, mostly near large rivers. And there are many small lakes scattered everywhere.

Phosphate mines operate in the White Springs area and farther north on US 411 near Jasper. Fossils are abundant in both areas and much Tampa Bay agate occurs there. Suwannee River State Park on US 90 is located at the confluence of the Withlacoochee and Suwannee Rivers. You can see exposures of Oligocene-age Suwannee limestone there. A little farther south near Ellaville you will find more exposure of Suwannee limestone.

Limestone quarries in Live Oak, Baldwin, and Old Town mine Ocala limestone. You can find a large selection of late Eocene fossils by searching available areas. Permission is necessary for hunting in quarries, but you can find many good specimens in nearby accessible area limestone. Sand dollars and sea urchins are common. Pockets of fossilized bones occasionally reveal land animals as well as marine fossils.

The upper part of the Suwannee River has a brooding primitive quality that changes as you follow the loop that takes you down toward Branford and the many nearby caverns. Cave diving instructors are readily available and you can find shops that sell diving gear. Rivers and caves can be exceedingly treacherous as well as very beautiful, so follow safety rules meticulously. Around Branford are several quarries in which you can find many marine fossils and shark's teeth, some of them silicified. You can also pick up coral fingers and geodes around these quarries.

When you hunt collectibles in Suwannee County, keep your eyes open for brief flashes of what looks like bright green malachite in the Dowling Park area. Since there has never been malachite reported officially in Florida, this green material is probably a bright green clay clast.

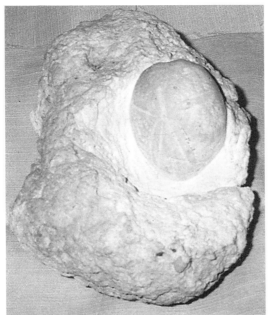

Echinoid found in a limestone quarry near Ocala, Marion County. From the collection of Jack Cummings. (Jack Cummings)

Fuller's earth mines are found in Gadsden County and Marion County, and deposits occur in sizable amounts near the surface. In the photo on page 34, taken in a fuller's earth mine by Dr. Tom Scott, Assistant State Geologist, the light gray area is fuller's earth. The rest is waste material; both would be good specimens in an industrial mineral collection.

Palygorskite, also known as attapulgite, is almost pure in high grade fuller's earth. Pure palygorskite has a special ability to gel and for this reason is valued as a paint thickener and for a similar use in some medicines. In lower grades, two other minerals may occur: a variety of montmorillonite and illite. Lower grade fuller's earth is also very useful in many products. This clay is used to absorb oil. It is also used as an additive in soaps, paints, and polishes. An important use of fuller's earth, as far as pet lovers worldwide are concerned, is its use as pet litter, particularly cat litter. That information might add a little zip to an otherwise matter-of-fact industrial mineral collection, especially for kids.

Geologists have a quick method for checking the presence of palygorskite: they touch their tongues to a piece of clay. It's a rough test, but if the tongue sticks to the clay, chances are pretty good the mineral is palygorskite or a mineral with a similar property, like kaolinite. Many ge-

A crowd gathers for one of the common sights in karst country such as central Florida: checking out another sinkhole. This one occurred in Ocala, Marion County. (Florida Geological Survey)

ologists have paid with a sore tongue for expediency in checking out clays in the field.

You can find good chert almost anywhere you search in Marion County. Many vertebrate fossils are found in widespread areas, but particularly in or near limestone quarries.

Anhydrite, usually found very deep in the rocks, has been found in some of the limestone mines in Marion County. Anhydrite is actually a deep de-watered gypsum. Gypsum is a calcium sulphate with a number of water molecules attached; anhydrite is just a calcium sulphate. Though rare, crystals of gypsum and anhydrite which have been replaced by silica have been dug up in quarries in Marion County. Both anhydrite and gypsum are found over a large part of the state, but at depths of several thousand feet or more.

Kaolin is composed of the clay mineral kaolinite, and Florida kaolin is highly regarded. Ceramic artists and artisans spend a great deal of time and effort searching out high-grade clay for their artistic projects, and they tend to guard their sources with care. Faculty members from fine arts departments of universities can be found gathering data on various clays in the field, as can many consulting geologists who specialize in clays suitable for art works. Kaolin is also used as filler in a variety of products from paints to tooth powder. Several counties in the central highlands have deposits of kaolin. A mine producing kaolin is in Edgar, in western Putnam County.

All through Alachua County you will be able to find good chert specimens and fossils. Two limestone quarries, one near Newberry and one near Gainesville, are able to net you concretions and fossils. Two sand and fill pits are also located near Gainesville. Permission to enter is necessary for any quarry or pit.

While you are in Gainesville, visit the Florida Museum of Natural History on Museum Road, University of Florida Campus. The reconstruction of a limestone cave is excellent and a fine collection of fossils is exhibited. In the same building a good bookstore offers a wide selection of titles, including some relating to natural history and paleontology subjects.

Thomas Farm, a very famous collecting site, is located in Gilchrist County, adjacent to Alachua County. You might want to inquire at the Florida Museum of Natural History while you are in or near Gainesville to find out when the next field trip for amateurs is being planned and whether you may accompany the group. Thomas Farm is a Miocene-age sinkhole that has yielded an enormous number of valuable fossils in more than 60 years of paleontological investigation and study.

The eastern part of Levy County is located in the Central Highlands Zone and the western portion in the Western Coastal Lowlands Zone. In Gulf Hammock there is a huge quarry. In the quarry site as well as some of the surrounding area, a very wide assortment of well-preserved fossils have been found: gastropods, quantities of shark teeth, echinoids, bryozoans, and corals, to name a few. This area is just off US 19 and US 98 at Gulf Hammock. Anywhere in Levy County you can find chert, some coral geodes, and other agatized shells.

Sumter is another county with good-quality chert for the finding, mostly around railroad and road cuts. Chert is found in the limestone quarries, too, along with a variety of fossils.

In February, 1994, an Orlando-based amateur fossil-hunting group was given a leg up on their fossil searches in the county—a year's lease—free. Their territory: a 30-foot clay pit that the county's road maintenance department had been using for years. Since clay is one of the best places to

An aerial view of a spectacular sinkhole that opened in downtown Winter Park, a wealthy city adjacent to Orlando. This photo was taken during a period when a paved street, a house, several businesses, three Porsches, a swimming pool—to mention only a few items—were still sliding into the white center of the voracious pit. (Florida Geological Survey)

look for fossils, their lease was very productive. Members of this group also found some rare teeth of a seven-gilled shark in a ditch in Winter Garden, a town near Orlando.

A rockhound would ordinarily consider his chances for prospecting success in a place like Orlando slim to zero. Even experienced collectors consider the area a combination of private property, county property, roads and tourist attractions. A county lease given to a paleontological group illustrates how important it is to check out local collecting clubs, no matter how improbably located they might seem. Keeping an up-to-date newspaper clipping file on geological subjects is another way to keep up with new developments.

Subscribe to the newsletters of rock and mineral clubs in areas you plan to visit and look for field trips to join. Examine field trip announcements from various fossil collecting and mineral collecting clubs around the state. The Bone Valley Fossil Society found chert, some nice calcite crystals, fossil echinoids like sea biscuits and sea urchins, and fossil shells in an authorized visit to a crushed stone plant in Brooksville.

In a midsummer newsletter sent by the Central Florida Mineral and

Gem Society was a notice that a field trip they planned to the Suwannee River had been postponed because of all the recent rain in that area. They expected to try for a September trip, that being a month more likely to be on the dry side. It was much better for a collector to find out this weather development via newsletter than via a spoiled trip.

For a city that is perched on top of an active karst terrain, geological excitement can be more immediate than interest in ancient bones. In May 1981, Winter Park, a small city adjacent to Orlando, suddenly developed a downtown sinkhole that gulped a house and shed, a Porsche sports car, half of the municipal swimming pool, several large oak trees, and two sections of streets nearby before it stabilized. Later three more Porsches, a pick-up camper, and the rear of an auto repair shop slid into the hole.

A huge domed cavity in Orlando aroused a great deal of interest 20 years ago. The rock dome, which acted as a ceiling to the cavity, was all that prevented many homes in the area from becoming instant lake-front property. The discovery of the cavity was made when a team of well-diggers were drilling for water. The drill pierced the dome and continued dropping unimpeded for 550 feet. Pumps drew water for 90 feet, then the level settled down to 12 feet of muck on the bottom as the water went back into the limestone. The crew capped the well, packed up their equipment and left; the well-digging project was abandoned.

Three blocks beyond this aborted effort lies a beautiful, round little lake named Lake Como. Lake Como began as a typical cavity in karst but in this case the dome caved in on a small cavity. A sinkhole formed and filled with water and Lake Como joined more than 7,800 other lakes that have formed in this manner.

Chapter 10

CENTRAL HIGHLANDS ZONE PHOSPHATE AREA

THE PHOSPHATE district of central Florida presents some eerie scenes, some craters-of-the-moon kinds of landscapes. Miles and miles of phosphate beds lie flat under the Florida sun, textured by pebbles of various sizes that lie scattered on a background of powdery material ranging in color from white to dark gray, dramatic but not pretty.

What is it about this drab, fascinating land that draws to it huge mining companies that invest in giant operations? What also draws to the same place scientists, geologists, and paleontologists? What draws dedicated amateurs willing to spend many hours broiling under the sun—and makes them consider themselves lucky to have the experience? What special motivation can mesmerize kids fortunate enough to be permitted there, and make them willing to burden themselves with heavy knapsacks loaded with rocks?

The geological area that has attracted all of these diversely impelled groups to central Florida is an area of four counties known as the Bone Valley Member of the Peace River Formation, Hawthorn Group. The name was given as a natural result of the bones and fossilized remains of creatures that inhabited this land in prehistoric times. Bone Valley was first reported by geologist J. Leidy in 1891 in his *A Description of Vertebrate Remains from Peace Creek, Florida.*

What draws miners and mining companies to Bone Valley is phosphate and the world market that consumes it. Phosphate production contrib-

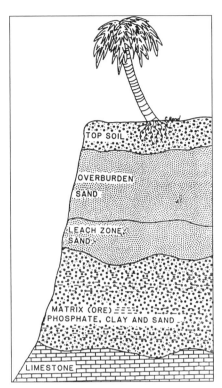

utes substantially to Florida's rating as fifth among mining states in the United States.

Figures shown in the latest book published by the United States Department of the Interior Bureau of Mines in 1993, indicate that in the whole United States, 16 companies produced $1.1 billion worth of marketable phosphate rock. Nine companies in Florida and one in North Carolina produced 86% of this phosphate rock. Most of this production (93%) went into fertilizer. Most of the rest was used to produce phosphoric acid and other phosphate chemicals.

With a financial stake like this, many mining companies are attracted to phosphate mining, but the numbers have dwindled from former years. Twenty mining companies used to operate mines in

ABOVE: *Sedimentary layering. This drawing illustrates the structure of land in the Florida phosphate district.* BELOW: *Looking into a phosphate mining area.* (Dan Behnke)

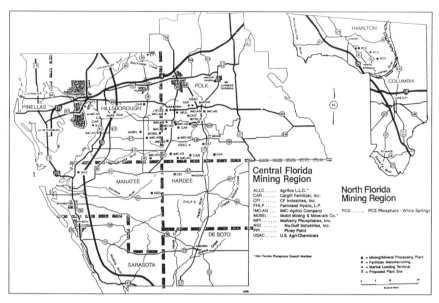

ABOVE: (Florida Phosphate Council)
BELOW: (Florida Geological Survey)

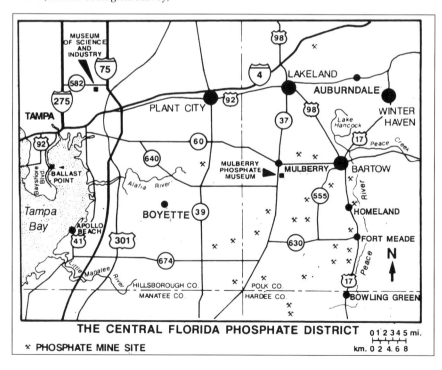

OPPOSITE TOP: *The Central and North Florida Mining District.*

BELOW: *The Central Florida Phosphate District. This map also shows two fine collecting sites, Ballast Point and Apollo Beach. The district shown here is famous for its numerous vertebrate fossils—both marine and terrestrial— abundant in phosphate mine spoil piles. Common finds are fish vertebrae, dugong ribs, turtle shell plates, and horse, camel, and mastodon teeth. Advance arrangements are needed to enter private mine property.*

RIGHT: *Distribution of phosphate in Florida.* (Florida Geological Survey)

BELOW: *This huge dragline, a phosphate mining machine, has a bucket capacity of 65 cubic yards. A dragline is used to remove the over-burden, or unwanted covering material, and excavate the phosphate matrix.* (Dan Behnke)

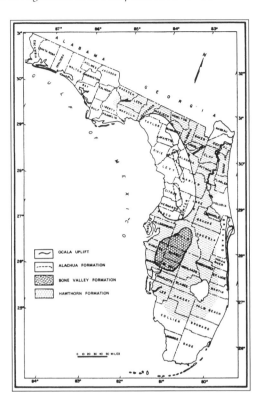

Cacoxenite spheres that occurred in Blue Springs Mine, Bartow. These particular spheres are 0.2mm in diameter. (Dan Behnke)

many different locations in more than eight counties. Now there are only five companies left. The others have merged or closed.

Along with the mines comes the attendant professional corps of mineralogists and geologists who work in the laboratories and the field.

In late years, more and more phosphate companies, required by Florida state law to set up environmental reclamation programs, have followed the lead of the pioneers like IMC Agrico Company, formerly known as International Minerals and Chemical Corporation and the Agrico Company. Hal Scott served as president of the Florida Audubon Society for a decade, and went on to become an environmental consultant; IMC Agrico was one of his clients.

Hal Scott contributed a great deal toward the company's outstanding reputation as an environmentally responsible company. After his death, IMC Agrico named their prize reclamation project after him as a memorial, the Hal Scott Wildlife Conservation Area. This wildlife refuge won a national award for reclamation.

IMC Fertilizer Company received the National Mined Land Reclamation Award from the National Association of State Land Reclamationists and in addition recently received First Place Award in the Land Restoration Category from the Florida Native Plant Society.

Scientists frequently gather in the phosphate area, singly or in concert.

Colorful Minerals of Florida

Wavellite, crystal, 12.4mm x 0.9mm.
Clear Spring Mine, Bartow. *Dan Behnke.*

Wavellite, crystals, 17.8mm x 0.3mm.
Clear Spring Mine, Bartow. *Dan Behnke.*

Wavellite, crystals, 11.7mm x 0.5mm.
Kingsford Mine, Bradley Junction.
Dan Behnke.

Wavellite, gold crystal masses, 4.3mm x
8.1mm. Phosphoria Mine. *Dan Behnke.*

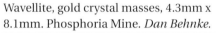

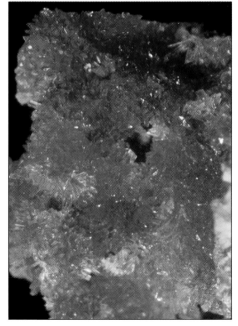

Chalcedony vug, bone with inclusions, 6.8mm x 3.9mm. Phosphoria Mine, Bartow. *Dan Behnke.*

Siderite crystal, 12.4mm x 0.56mm, center crystal, Bartow. *Dan Behnke.*

Siderite, 4.3mm x 2.3mm sphere, Bartow. *Dan Behnke.*

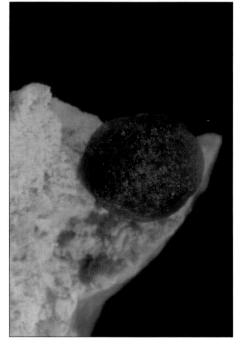

ABOVE: Vivianite branched crystal.
Clear Spring Mine, Bartow.
BELOW: Vivianite cluster. Clear Spring
Mine. *Both photos, Anthony Gricius.*
TOP RIGHT: Vivianite, crystal, 3.5mm;
center crystal, 1cm. Clear Spring
Mine. *Anthony Gricius.*
BELOW RIGHT: Mitridatite/vivianite
nodule, 2.3mm x 15.6mm.
Phosphoria Mine, Bartow.
Dan Behnke.

Calcite crystal, 4.3mm x 3.2mm. Fort Lonesome. *Dan Behnke.*

Calcite on dolomite,
6.8mm x 1.9mm. Bartow.
Dan Behnke.

Calcite. *Thomas M. Scott.*

Stalactites in Florida Caverns. *Thomas M. Scott.*

Calcite lecanto. *Ken Campbell.*

Orange calcite. *Thomas M. Scott.*

Calcite crystal cluster-gold.
Thomas M. Scott.

Calcite crystal cluster.
Thomas M. Scott.

Vivianite nodule, 3.6mm x 8.2mm. Clear Spring Mine, Bartow.
Dan Behnke.

Vivianite group crystal, 5.9mm x 3.2mm. Clear Spring Mine, Bartow.
Dan Behnke.

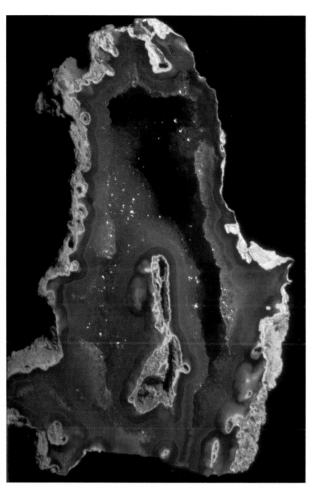

Agatized coral.
Michael M. Smith.

Agatized coral found in the
Withlacoochee River in
Hernando County.
Charles Howlett collection.
Michael M. Smith.

Three specimens of coral found in the
Tampa Bay area. Charles Howlett
collection. *Michael M. Smith.*

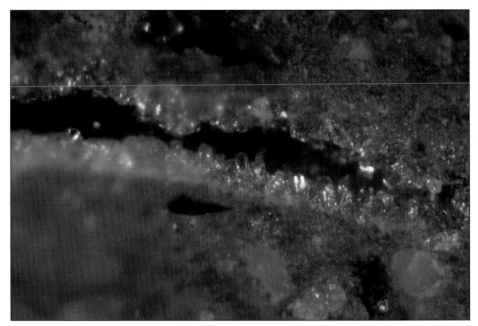

Apatite crystal, 2.0mm x 1.75mm. Clear Spring Mine, Bartow. *Dan Behnke.*

Autunite crystal, 0.96mm. Noralyun Mine, Bartow. *Dan Behnke.*

Strunzite crystals from Blue Springs Mine. These crystals measure about 0.56mm in diameter. (Dan Behnke)

Sometimes they come to examine and evaluate for their various reasons the mineral properties of material mined; sometimes to examine damage found and to find remedies; sometimes to offer ways to heal and restore the land.

Incredible numbers of paleontological finds have been made in the area, some sufficiently important to receive wide media attention. Less

A wavelite cluster from Clear Springs Mine. The center cluster measures 4.6mm in diameter. (Dan Behnke)

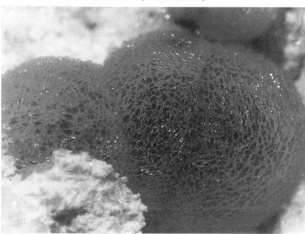

Wavellite, found at Clear Springs Mine. This crystal measures 1.5cm long. (Dr. James B. Murowchick)

spectacular discoveries have delighted generations of wide-eyed children as well as adults who find joy in the ancient gifts of the earth.

Secondary minerals are minerals that form later than the rock enclosing them, from the primary mineral material. In the phosphate district, primary material is the mixture of apatite, quartz sand, and clays. Secondary minerals form as a result of weathering, or activity caused by metamorphic or solution forces. A very exciting find is the discovery of sparkling crystals that formed as secondary minerals among more industrially valued primary minerals.

The names of the Bone Valley secondary crystals are musical, to a point that you could say that in the melody of minerals, the crystals are grace notes, elegant, small, fragile, and exquisitely beautiful.

The Bone Valley Member of the Central Highlands Zone is limited to Polk, Hillsborough, Manatee, and Hardee counties. Several neighboring counties, however, share a wealth of fossils and minerals: Sarasota, De Soto, Highlands, and Osceola. Commercial mining today occurs only in five counties of central Florida: Polk, Hillsborough, Manatee, Hardee, and De Soto.

Geologically, Bone Valley gravel lies at the top of the Hawthorn Group and is covered by Pleistocene terrace sands. The phosphate ore of Bone Valley is an approximately equally proportioned mixture of quartz sand, clays, and apatite. In addition to this ore product (a carbonate fluoroapatite), weathering has produced unusual iron and aluminum

Stingray tail spines and dermal plates found in Polk County. From the collection of Jack Cummings. (Michael Smith)

TOP: *Lower jaw bones and molars of a tapir, Polk County.* BOTTOM: *Front of a tapir's lower jaw, with the canine teeth. Both Pleistocene, Polk County. From the collection of Jack Cummings.* (Michael Smith)

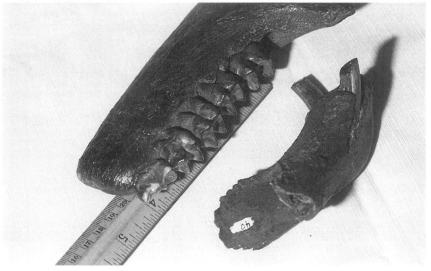

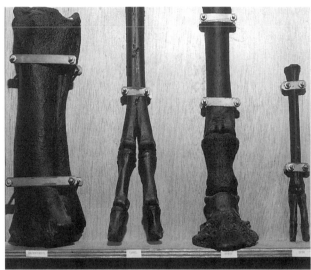

ABOVE: *Fossilized bones found in Polk County. From left, fibula of a rhinoceros, front leg of a camel, front leg of a horse* (equus), *front leg of a deer. From the collection of Jack Cummings.*

BELOW: *Bony dermal armor of edentates, armadillos, and glyptotherium. These Pleistocene fossils were found in Hillsborough County. From the collection of Jack Cummings.* (Michael Smith photos)

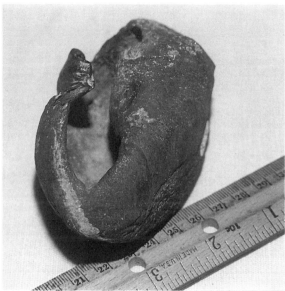

The inner ear bone of a large whale, found in Polk County. From the collection of Jack Cummings. (Michael Smith)

phosphates—creating secondary minerals of sometimes startling beauty.

These secondary phosphate minerals are common in the leached zone (see the simplified drawing of sediment layering on page 93). But they can be found in other zones, too. Sometimes they are found as minute occurrences, sometimes as microscopic crystals. Some secondary minerals are found in veins, some in pockets, and some coat other minerals to form stunning miniature partnerships.

Photography of these microscopic crystals has become an art form among collectors and geologists who specialize in micro-photography and macro-photography. Prize-winning photographers like Dan Behnke and Anthony Gricius have made secondary minerals from the phosphate district famous.

Thomas H. Scott and James B. Murowchick have used macro-photography in many photographs. You will find examples of their work in this book. Because each photographer has a preference in equipment and supplies, as well as methods, your own camera supply store is the place to examine what is available and to determine what suits you. Photographs like these are almost always done under studio conditions so equipment including lenses must be chosen with that in mind.

A list of phosphate minerals photographed by Dan Behnke and Anthony Gricius includes the following:

APATITE occurs as fragments, pellets and minute druses. It may line cavities. Colors include white, black, brown, and tan.

AUTUNITE is rare. The only occurrence was reported in altered rock in the form of small square tablets, highly fluorescent.

BERAUNITE occurs in iron-rich caprock. Colors include dark green and red oxidized varieties.

CACOXENITE is found in association with beraunite. Color is yellow. Crystals are minute fibrous spheroids. They can be found in nearly pure masses within porous red iron oxides.

CRANDALLITE occurs replacing apatite. It is common in the lower part of the leached zone. However, in good crystals, this mineral is very rare. Even crystals as tiny as the ones photographed are very rare. They are high in aluminum, which interferes with the mining process.

STRENGITE occurs associated with rockbridgeite, beraunite, and cacoxenite. Its only confirmed locality is at the Clear Springs Mine.

ROCKBRIDGEITE occurs as nodules. They are common in iron caprock immediately overlying a leached zone. Colors include greenish to black. Usually nodules are altered and contain minute crystals or aggregates of beraunite, cacoxenite, ferroan-variscite, wavellite, cyrilovite, strengite, phosphosiderite, strunzite, and vivianite.

STRUNZITE occurs as minute yellow fibrous crystals. It resembles cacoxenite.

VIVIANITE occurs in two ways. It may occur as an alteration of iron phosphates in the caprock, with crystals that are small and generally altered to a deep blue to black. Rarely, it may occur as bright green crystals in open pockets.

Vivianite may also occur at the base of a pit just above underlying dolomite. First reported by Watson and Gooch in 1918, the next report occurred in 1980 when transparent green terminated crystals up to 3cm were found. They occurred in pockets and open seams in massive recrystalized apatite.

Vivianite is photo-sensitive and if specimens are kept too long in the light they will lose their gemmy quality and turn a steely dull gray. For this reason, tuck your vivianite away in a dark place except for viewing time.

Bernard L. Murowchick, who was Chief Mineralogist at IMC at the time of the vivianite discovery, tells the story of a find—an exciting occasion.

The plant metallurgist entered his office, holding a piece of rock and said, "What is this green thing? We found it in a slurry pit." A slurry pit is where the dragline dumps the phosphate ore. After a hydraulic stream breaks it up, it is pumped to the plant.

"Let's check the dry well," Bernard Murowchick suggested, knowing that the dragline operator moves along, mining as far as he can reach, after which he moves to a new location. He leaves behind the last slurry pit, which in due time dries out, often leaving exposed fossils and minerals.

They hurried to the last dry well. Lying around were chunks of cream-colored rock, some with vivianite crystals gleaming green in the sunlight. Quickly they went down into the pit, 40 or 50 feet deep. Collectors were already in the pit, digging into the sides and the outcropping, looking for seams that were open and had crystals in them—there was no time to waste.

As the dragline mines, usually a dam is built to keep nearby areas from flooding the pit. A pump in the pit keeps the water out of the mine. As work moves along, the latest location is allowed to fill up with water.

There were tense minutes before the decision was made to protect the site temporarily. Pumps were kept at the location and for several months the pit was kept dry. In a scientific report of the vivianite occurrence, C. L. Himes and B. L. Murowchick discussed discovering ironstone formations with vivianite and repeated occurrence of microcrystalline beraunite, crandallite, cacoxenite, siderite, and wavellite.

They reported well-formed light-green vivianite crystals turned blue-green quickly upon exposure to light or abrasion. The color proved stable in well-formed crystals but less well-crystallized specimens continued altering to translucent dark blue or black. A second type of deposit produced vivianite that was initially darker green.

The professionals have no illusions about the elusiveness of their mineral quarry. The vivianite report ends stoically, "Due to mine and fill methods used in the phosphate industry, the areas reported here are inaccessible. No further vivianite has been encountered as operations have moved to southern portions of the phosphate district."

The lure of making a discovery of importance keeps people trying, though, as any rockhound knows. Amateur fossil hunter Larry Martin made his once-in-a-lifetime find in a wet phosphate trench in Polk County. He was hunting in mines about 25 miles south of Lakeland. Usually he searched through excavated phosphate, keeping out of the workers' way.

On his one special day he decided to dig in freshly cut mine trenches 40 feet below the surface of the earth. He saw some teeth and a ridge of bone and carried home what turned out to be a skull. He started cleaning the skull with dental picks and brushes, then called the University of Florida and spoke to fossil expert Dr. Bruce MacFadden, who identified the skull as the only horse skull dug up in west central Florida in more than a hundred years. In addition, it was said to be the only horse skull known of its particular species. The skull was six inches long and identified as *Nannipus minor* (dwarf horse), a tiny three-toed horse which stood about three feet tall and is considered second smallest of the sixteen varieties that roamed the southern United States. At the time of the find, Museum Curator Bruce MacFadden judged the skull to be 5 million years old. This skull will join other donations to the University of Florida Museum of a great number of teeth and bones of other creatures Larry Martin has discovered.

Youngsters find fossils in the phosphate district, too. Duane Turner regularly makes hunting trips to the Fort Meade area with his father. A trip when he was a third-grader netted him three buckets full of fossils. Among about two hundred separate items, his finds ranged from shark teeth to vertebrae from a *Cetotheres* (baleen whale), one from *Pomatodelphis* (a small dolphin with a very long beak), and ribs from an extinct sea cow, as identified by paleontologist Gary Morgan in a formal report from the department of Vertebrate Paleontology, Florida Museum of Natural History.

While none of these finds added new information to existing data, Duane Turner's accomplishments are very important. His fossils are on display at Skeen Elementary School in Leesburg and gifts from his collection to other collectors have become the nucleus of dozens of new collections (see photograph on page 22).

All of the mines have security people and patrols. If you are interested in prospecting for minerals and fossils, you must make arrangements first. Field trips for Scouts, schools, clubs for rock and mineral collectors and paleontological clubs—all these are encouraged and can be arranged. Information about phosphates and phosphate mining is available at the **Florida Phosphate Council;** Write to **Elin Oak, P.O. Box 367, Lakeland, FL 33802.** See the Appendix for a list of Florida Phosphate Council members and the companies with which they are affiliated as well as their addresses.

At the present time requests for information and permission to collect are handled through the office of the Mulberry Phosphate Museum, rather than by inquiries addressed to individual mining companies in the area. Inquiries should be addressed to the **Mulberry Phosphate Museum, Lewetta Haag, Curator, Mulberry, FL 33860.** The Museum is open Tuesday through Saturday from 10 am to 4:30 pm; no admission charge.

You might also check into a membership with the **Bone Valley Fossil Society.** The membership dues are low, the quality of the newsletter is consistently high, and activities are very interesting. People from other cities are members so with a little extra effort car pools can be arranged. The current president of the organization, Lou Harvey, lives in Orlando, for instance. To inquire about the Bone Valley Fossil Society write **Lou Harvey, 2102 Monastery Circle, Orlando, FL 32822.**

No limit exists on the ages of people who can participate in rock collecting. From toddlers picking up shark teeth on the sands of a Gulf coast beach to their great-grandparents picking over crystals in a shell pit in Seminole County, any member of a family can find a compatible companion for the hunt. Background or education has little to do with either your success or your enjoyment. The operative attitude is interest and a driving need to become better acquainted with the earth's crust, to know at least some of the rocks and minerals and fossils that are buried in it or lie on it. When you feel like that, you're already one of Florida's rockhounds, ready to pick up your packed-for-action knapsack and hit the collecting trail intent on geological treasure. And you will probably find it.

GLOSSARY

AGATE (*aka* Tampa Bay agate, Miami agate): Both agate and chalcedony composed of cryptocrystalline (needs stronger magnification than magnifying glass to be seen) silica. Ballast Point, Florida is world-famous for agatized pseudomorphs after coral. Agatized fossils found along Gulf Coast and phosphate mines. Colors usually arranged in parallel bands.

ANHYDRITE: A deep de-watered gypsum, occurs as a calcium sulphate. Texture like marble, usually no crystals. Occurs deep in subsurface and is usually seen in well cores. Colors: brown, gray, white.

APATITE: Widespread as fine-grained clasts, pellets. Some minute druzes of colorless crystals lining cavities in recrystalized apatite.

ARAGONITE: Relatively unstable form of calcium carbonate. Associated with gypsum in deep wells; interesting form, as iridescent lining in shells.

BALLAST ROCK: Rock brought into Florida on ships as ballast.

BONE VALLEY MEMBER: *Bone Valley* is a unit name in FGS nomenclature, not a place name.

BRYOZOANS: (*Schizoporella Floridans*): *aka* sea mats because they mat on fossils and shells, forming colonies with complex structures. Abundant as fossils, they are also plentiful as living creatures in modern seas.

CALCITE: Calcium carbonate. Commonly occurs in limestone; principal mineral in seashells (recent and fossil); colors vary from white to shades of yellow, orange, and gray. More than 300 crystal forms have been described.

CAST: Results from filling a mold, either natural or artificial, with a substance. *Natural cast* occurs when mold is filled under natural conditions while still imbedded in rock. *Artificial cast* or *replica* occurs when mold is filled with wax, plaster, acrylic, or rubber.

CENOZOIC: Age of Mammals, 65 million years ago to present time.

CHALCEDONY (see agate): Both agate and chalcedony are composed of cryptocrystalline silica with colors arranged in parallel bands.

CHERT (also known in Florida as flint or flint rock): Very hard (7.0), conchoidal or shell-like fracture. A variety of fine-grained quartz, chert was formed by replacement of calcium carbonate with silica carried in moving ground water.

CLASTIC: Fragments of older rocks.

CONCRETIONS: Hardened masses of minerals weathered to look like fossils.

CONCHOIDAL: Fracture in a sea-shell shape.

COQUINA: A soft whitish limestone; contains marine shell fragments, corals and sometimes quartz sand. Calcite is principal cementing agent. Coquina gets harder as it weathers; it "case-hardens."

CORAL: Tiny marine animal with external skeleton of calcium carbonate; most grow in colonies as bottom-dwellers. Some are solitary. Abundant as fossils, they also form living colonies in modern seas.

CRYSTALS: Most minerals can form crystals when conditions are right. These sharp-cornered, flat-faced shapes are as special to minerals as human fingerprints. There are thirty-two distinct crystal classes which are assigned to six main crystal systems: isometric, hexagonal, tetragonal, orthorhombic, monoclinic, and triclinic.

DOLOMITE (also called dolostone): Usually associated with limestone. Composed of calcite and magnesium carbonate.

ECHINOID: Free-moving echinoderms, disc shaped, heart shaped, biscuit shaped and globular. Food grooves on shell show typical five-rayed star pattern. Abundant as fossils. Modern echinoids include sea urchins, sand dollars, and heart urchins.

EPICENTER: Point on the earth's surface directly above an earthquake's *focus* (where the quake's energy originates below the surface).

FLINT: Dense sedimentary rock. *Aka* chert in Florida.

FORAMINIFERA: Mostly microscopic-sized one-celled animals with calcium carbonate shells. Helped build many limestones.

FOSSIL: Traces, remains of ancient life forms preserved by natural processes.

FULGURITE (from Greek word for lightning): Formed when lightning fuses sand into shape of lightning path.

FULLER'S EARTH *(aka attapulgite, palygorskite)*: In Florida, an earth-clay mix of palygorskite, varieties of montmorillonite and sometimes, illite. Color: blue to gray to light gray-green.

GASTROPOD: Largest group of mollusks; includes snails, slugs, whelks, and abalones. Both fossil and modern shells show great variety in size, shape, and ornamentation.

GEODE: Hollow rounded rock or nodule with crystals formed inside.

GYPSUM: A calcium sulphate with a number of water molecules attached.

GEOMORPHOLOGY: The configuration and history of landforms and geologic change; relationship of underlying changes to surface features.

HEAVY MINERALS: Minerals with specific gravities greater than quartz. In Florida heavy minerals are sand-sized. Examples: zircon, ilmenite, rutile, monazite, garnet, kyanite, leucoxene, sillimanite, andalusite, pyroxene, corundum, spinel, epidote, tourmaline, staurolite. Monazite is a phosphate mineral that is listed among several rare earth metals.

IGNEOUS ROCK: Produced by fire or extreme heat; granite (found in Florida at great depths); volcanic rock (found in Florida as basement rocks in general region of Collier County, ages Late Triassic—Early Jurassic.) No igneous rock exposed at surface in Florida.

IMPRESSIONS: Certain traces of plants and animals accepted as fossils: tracks and trails, molds and casts, coprolites, borings and burrows, stomach stones.

IRON: Pyrite is an iron sulphate which sometimes occurs in dolomite or dolostone deposits in Florida.

KAOLIN: *kaolinite,* clay mineral.

KARST: Region distinguished by chemical weathering of carbonate rocks (limestone, dolomite, gypsum) producing many caves, sinks, sinkholes, and lakes. Name came from the Karst District in Jugaslavia.

KNAPPING: Striking a stone with a short sharp blow. This is a technique used by Native Americans to shape chert into sharp-edged weapons and tools.

LIMESTONE: *Key Largo Limestone, Miami Limestone, Ocala Limestone, Oolithic Limestone, Suwannee Limestone, Tamiami Limestone.*

LIMONITE: (*aka* bog iron): A brown hematite occurring as yellow ochre, a soft clayey material.

MARL: Crumbly stratum, mostly sand, clay, and calcium carbonate.

MERCALLI (MM): Levels of earthquake shock intensity based on human observations; given in Roman numerals and ranging from MMI to MMXII.

METAMORPHIC: Change in rock structure and form; caused by heat, pressure, water, results in crystallization, possible obliteration, condensation etc. No metamorphic rocks exposed on surface in Florida; some at several thousand feet in wells.

MIOCENE: 5 million to 24.5 million years ago.

MOLDS: Impression of organism in surrounding material. *External mold:* impression left of outside surface. *Internal mold:* impression formed when sediment fills vacated shell.

MOLLUSCAN (also mollusks; molluscan facies): referring to mollusca, a large phylum of invertebrates including clams, slugs, snails, oysters, whelks, etc. With soft body and calcareous shell parts.

NODULE: Rounded concretionary mineral mass.

NUCLEATION: Formed into or around a nucleus; beginning of crystal growth involving one or more points.

OOLITHIC (also ooids, oolite, oolitic limestone, oolitic rock): made up of sedimentary rock formed by the bodies of ooliths. Oolith bodies are rounded and look rather like fish eggs cemented together.

OPAL: Glassy translucent silica; various colors; values differ.

PALEONTOLOGY: Branch of geology dealing with prehistoric life through study of plant and animal fossils.

PHOSPHATE TERMS: *Benefication:* Separating wanted mineral from other material in the matrix, such as separating clay and sand from phosphate. *Dragline:* Large machine used in excavation, in phosphate buckets to 65 cubic yards capacity. *Phosphate rock:* Mineral containing the element phosphorous. *Slurry:* Mixture of water and solid material.

PSEUDOMORPHS: Calcite replacing original siliceous parts. Forms a natural cast (*calcareous pseudomorphs).*

PYRITE: Iron sulfide. Also called fool's gold. Florida crystals small.

PLEISTOCENE EPOCH: A Cenozoic epoch just preceding the recent Holocene; from 10 thousand to 1.8 million years ago.

QUARTZ: Crystalline mineral, silicon dioxide; variety of colors.

RICHTER: Measure of earthquake magnitude; measures seismic waves and is related to amount of energy released. Magnitudes expressed in whole numbers and decimals.

SECONDARY MINERAL: Mineral found later than rock enclosing it. Usually it is formed at expense of earlier primary minerals.

SEDIMENTARY: All surface rock in Florida is sedimentary.

SEISMIC: Having to do with an earthquake.

SELENITE: A kind of gypsum.

SILICA: Silicon dioxide, a hard glassy mineral; found in sand, opal, quartz etc.

SLAG: Refuse or dross from smelting.

SLOTH *(eremotherium):* Ice-age mammal whose fossils were found in Leisey Shell Pit.

SPELEOLOGY: Scientific study and exploring of caves and caverns involving a wide range of activities and disciplines. **Associated terms:** *troglodytes*—cave dwellers in prehistoric times, cave protectors in this time. *Dry cave*—a cave which can be explored without use of SCUBA or snorkel gear. *Wet cave*—underwater cave which requires special gear and training for cavers. *Speleothems*—formations in caves caused by mineral deposits: dripstone, cave pearls etc. See: *stalactite, stalagmite.*

SPICULES: Small, hard, needle-like parts; often calcareous piece of sponge skeleton.

SPOIL PILES AND ISLANDS: Unwanted material dredged by construction for ship channels, drainage ditches, other such excavations.

STALACTITES: Formed by precipitation of calcium carbonate, which produces downward growth of calcite stalactites from cracks or openings in cave ceilings.

STALAGMITES: Formed by excess water dripping to floor of cave, precipitating calcite which grows upward from the cave floor. In time it may join the stalactite growing above it, forming a column.

STELLATE: Crystals which aggregate in a star-shaped ray pattern, similar to wavellite.

TAILINGS: Waste or refuse from a mining operation.

TANNIN: Tannic acid, a yellowish astringent from oak bark, nuts, and similar staining substances.

VERTEBRATE: Animals with a backbone or spinal column.

VUG: A cavity or hollow in rock, often lined with crystals.

ZIRCON: Heavy mineral found in small grains in Florida.

APPENDIX A:
GEM, MINERAL, AND FOSSIL CLUBS

Many of the gem and mineral and fossil clubs of Florida are affiliated with the Eastern Federation of Mineralogical & Lapidary Societies, Inc. and the American Federation of Mineralogical Societies.

The current treasurer of E.F.M.L.S. is located in Orlando, Florida:
Sybil Churchwell
2005 Rockwell Road
Orlando, FL 32808
(407) 295-8967
Information about the A.F.M.S. can be obtained by writing to the secretary: Dan Mc Lennan
P.O. Box 26523
Oklahoma City, OK 73126-0523
(405) 525-2692

Local gem and mineral clubs routinely print and distribute their own newsletters; in addition, they receive and reprint newsletter items from their affiliates and fellow clubs. This gives you access to a wide variety of information when you join a gem and mineral and fossil club in your own locality. Some of the items usually covered in your local club newsletter are safety tips, current legislation and conservation efforts, shows and swaps, and tips on finding and handling various geological collectibles.

Many clubs own or have members who own equipment for gem or stone cutting and polishing. This equipment is frequently made available to members for a small fee, which gives you an opportunity to try out lapidary activities without a big investment. Faceting and cabochon workshops are often conducted on a regular basis as part of club activities. Shows and swaps offer an opportunity to sell hand-crafted jewelry and items no longer wanted in your own collection.

Books and periodicals can be shared and borrowed by members and often specialty magazines such as *Lapidary Journal* offer a return of part of your subscription price to your club. This helps finance club activities such as field trips and various workshops.

Notices of upcoming shows routinely appear in club newsletters as do notices of shows occurring in other parts of the United States.

Some gem and mineral and fossil clubs have permanent meeting places; others do not, and instead will meet at the homes of members or otherwise have changes of location. Local museums and libraries will have information on local organizations.

The following Active Gem and Mineral and Fossil organizations are currently listed with E.F.M.L.S. in Florida:

Bone Valley Fossil Society, Inc.
2704 Dixie Road,
Lakeland, Florida 33601

Central Florida Mineral and Gem Society
P.O. Box 536111
Orlando, Florida 32853

Florida Panhandle Gem and Mineral Society
P.O. Box 531
Pensacola, Florida 32593

Gem and Mineral Society of the Palm Beaches, Inc.
P.O. Box 3041
West Palm Beach, Florida 33402

Gulf Coast Mineral, Fossil and Gem Club, Inc.
P.O. Box 1404
Venice, Florida 34284

Manasota Rock and Gem Club, Inc.
P.O. Box 5872
Sarasota, Florida 342777-5872

Miami Mineral and Gem Society
P.O. Box 558172
Miami, Florida 33155

Miami Mineralogical and Lapidary Guild, Inc.
3280 So. Miami Avenue
Miami, Florida 33129

Panama City Gem and Mineral Society, Inc.
1204 East 3rd Street
Panama City, Florida 32401

Playground Gem and Mineral Society
P.O. Box 598
Fort Walton Beach, Florida 32549

Southeast Florida Gem, Mineral and Fossil Club
13302 4th Street, S.E.
Fort Myers, Florida 33905

Tampa Bay Mineral and Science Club
P.O. Box 15176
Tampa, Florida 33614

Other gem, mineral, and fossil organizations in Florida include:

Brooksville: **Withlacoochee Rockhounds**
Clearwater: **West Central Florida Gem & Mineral Association**
 Pinellas Geological Society
Daytona Beach: **Tomoka Gem & Mineral Club**
Fort Pierce: **St. Lucie County Rock & Gem Club**
Jacksonville: **Jacksonville Gem & Mineral Society**
Melbourne: **Canaveral Mineral & Gem Society**
Miami: **South Florida Mineral, Fossil, Gem Society**
New Port Richey: **Anclote Earth Science Club**
St. Petersburg: **Suncoast Gem & Mineral Society**
Tampa: **Tampa Bay Fossil Club**
Titusville: **Central Brevard Rock & Gem Club**
Vero Beach: **Treasure Coast Rock & Gem Society**
Winter Haven: **Imperial Polk County Gem & Mineral Society**

APPENDIX B
ROCK, MINERAL, AND FOSSIL MUSEUMS AND EXHIBITS

Natural history museums are plentiful in Florida, from large and well-known and publicized institutions to museums in schools and colleges, displays in universities, and children's museums which are more limited in scope. Many state parks also have fine exhibits. Some of these displays are listed below.

NORTHERN FLORIDA

Museum of Florida History
500 S. Bronough Street
Tallahassee, Florida
Displays: Wakulla mastodon skeleton; Native American artifacts.

Florida Geological Survey
Corner of Woodward and Tennessee Streets
Tallahassee, Florida
Displays: Variety of Florida rocks and minerals; Miocene dugong. Survey
library supplies publications on Florida geology upon request.

GULF COAST

Museum of Science and Industry
4801 East Fowler Avenue
Tampa, Florida
Displays: Florida fossil and mineral collections.

South Florida Museum and Bishop Planetarium
US 41 and 10th Street
W. Bradenton, Florida
Displays: Excellent shell and fossil collections; variety of vertebrates.

PHOSPHATE DISTRICT

Mulberry Phosphate Museum
Downtown Mulberry: 1 block south of State Highway 60
on State Highway 37.
Displays: Variety of fossils found in nearby mines; material relating to phosphate mining. Small museum. Hospitable, delightful. Keeps a pile of phosphate material outside so visitors can prospect for fossils.

Florida Museum of Natural History
Museum Road, University of Florida campus
Gainesville, Florida
Displays: Diorama showing recovery of Bone Valley fossils; excellent fossil displays; reconstruction of Florida limestone cave.

SOUTHERN FLORIDA

The Conservancy Nature Center
1450 Merrihue Drive
Naples, Florida
Displays: Collection of fossil mollusks; fossil vertebrates.

South Florida Science Museum
4801 Dreher Trail North
West Palm Beach, Florida
Displays: Vertebrate fossils.

EASTERN COAST

Fred Dana Marsh Museum, Tomoka State Park
State Road AlA, 3 miles north of Ormond Beach, Florida
Displays: Geological cross-section of Florida; succession of dunes and lagoons.

Museum of Arts and Sciences
1040 Museum Blvd.
Daytona Beach, Florida
Displays: Giant ground sloth fossil (Eremotherium); other local fossils.

Gillespie Museum of Minerals
Stetson University Campus
Deland, Florida
Displays: Collection of minerals; some local specimens.

Lightner Museum
75 King Street
St. Augustine, Florida
Displays: Exhibit of rocks and minerals; fossils

Orlando Science Center
810 E. Rollins Avenue
Orlando, Florida
Displays and activities; rocks and minerals; additional exhibits planned.

Jacksonville Museum of Sciences and History
1025 Gulf Life Drive
Jacksonville, Florida
Displays: Rocks and minerals and a variety of fossils.

APPENDIX C
ADDITIONAL INFORMATION RESOURCES
ON FLORIDA GEOLOGY

Earthquakes

Earthquakes and Seismic History of Florida. Ed Lane. Open File Report No. 40. Florida Geological Survey, February 1991.

"Earthquake History of Florida: 1727 to 1981." *Florida Scientist,* Vol. 46, pp. 116-120.

History of Seismological Activity in Florida. D. L. Smith and A. F. Randazzo. 1989. Electric Power Research Institute Document EPRI NP-6437-D, pp. 2-37 to 2-58.

Mining and Industrial Minerals

The Industrial Minerals Industry Directory of Florida. Steven M. Spencer. Information Circular No. 109. Florida Geological Survey, 1993.

Radon Potential Study, Alachua County Florida by K. M. Campbell, P.G., and T. M. Scott, P.G. Open File Report No. 41. Florida Geological Survey, 1991.

Florida. Doss H. White, Jr., and Walter Schmidt. U.S. Department of the Interior, Bureau of Mines, 1991.

Mineral Commodity Summaries. United States Department of the Interior, Bureau of Mines, 1993

Florida: The New Uranium Producer. John W. Sweeney and Steve R. Windham. 1979. In cooperation with U.S. Dept. of the Interior, Bureau of Mines; from a presentation at the 1979 AIME Annual Meeting, New Orleans, LA, February 18-22, 1969.

Fossils

Fossil Book. Carol Lane Fenton and Mildred Adams Fenton. Doubleday, 1989.

The Practical Paleontologist. Steve and Benor Parker. Simon and Schuster/Firestone, 1990.

Paleontology: The Record of Life. C. W. Stern and R. I. Carroll. Wiley, 1989.

Fossils. William H. Matthews III. Barnes & Noble, 1962.

Fossil Vertebrates. M. C. Thomas. Beach and Bank Collecting for Amateurs, 1984.

Vertebrate Paleontology. Alfred S. Romer. University of Chicago Press, 1966.

The Avifauna of the Bone Valley Formation. Pierce Brodkorb. Dept. of Biology, Univ. of Florida, Gainesville, 1965.

Speleology References

NSS Cavern Diving Manual. John L. Zumrick, Jr., M.D., J. Joseph Prosser, and H. V. Grey. A really excellent book by three outstanding experts in the field;

info on cave terminology, formation; diving equipment; buoyancy control, propulsion; emergency procedures; detailed student outline guide for *Cavern Diver Course.* NACD-NSS publication, Branford, FL, 1988.

Hand Signals for Diving. Claudette Finley, Jaime Stone, Carol Vilece. NACD-NSS Gainesville, FL, 1986.

Visiting American Caves. Howard N. Sloane and Russell H. Gurnee. Endorsed by The National Speleological Society. Bonanza Books, 1966.

Caving Basics. G. Thomas Rea, ed. Comprehensive guide for beginning cavers. NSS publication, 1992.

Manual of U.S. Cave Rescue Techniques. Steve Hudson, ed. Covers search and rescue, medical and transport techniques, equipment. NSS publication.

General References

Land from the Sea: The Geologic Story of South Florida. John Edward Hoffmeister. University of Miami Press, 1974.

Guide to Rocks and Minerals of Florida. Ed Lane. Florida Geological Survey, 1987.

History of the Earth. Bernhard Kummel, Harvard University. W. H. Freeman & Company, 1961.

Natural Regions of the United States and Canada. Charles B. Hunt, Johns Hopkins University. W. H. Freeman Company, 1974.

Gem Hunter's Guide. Russell P. MacFall. Thomas Y. Crowell Company, 1969.

Dana's Manual of Mineralogy. Wiley. Current edition.

Karst in Florida. Ed Lane. Florida Geological Survey, 1986.

The Rockhound's Handbook. James R. Mitchell. Gem Guides Book Co., 1996.

Additional Florida Geological Survey Information

The List of Publications published by the Florida Geological Survey is revised and expanded from time to time, so get the latest edition available. Address all orders and correspondence to:

Florida Geological Survey
903 W. Tennessee Street
Tallahassee, Fl. 32304-7700
Attn: Publications

Wonderful environmental geology and hydrogeology publications are available; county by county publications detailing geological features and history; map series in the Environmental Geology Series giving valuable precise information of earth structure. Another fine map series deals with the mineral resources of various counties. Special areas of reports: Sinkholes: Type, Development and Distribution; Wetlands; Aquifers; Terraces and Shorelines; Geology booklets on State Parks: Florida Keys, Torreya, St. George Island, St.

Joseph Peninsula, St. Andrews and Grayton Beach; Suwannee River, Tchetacknee Springs, O'Leno and Manatee Springs; Wakulla Springs, Falling Waters, to name a few. Posters also are available.

These publications are offered at nominal cost by the Geological Survey. Publications are also sent to certain libraries in Florida and the public is encouraged to use the references. These libraries are:

Bartow: Florida Institute of Phosphate Research Library
Boca Raton: Florida Atlantic University Library
Clearwater: St. Petersburg Jr. College
Cocoa: Brevard County Public Library
Coral Gables: University of Miami Library
Dania: Nova University Library
Daytona Beach: Museum of Arts & Sciences Library
    Volusia County Library System
DeFuniak Springs: Walton-DeFuniak Library
Deland: Stetson University Library
Fort Lauderdale: Broward County Library System
    Broward Community College
Fort Myers: University of South Florida, Fort Myers Campus
    Lee County Library System
Fort Pierce: St. Lucie County Library
Gainesville: University of Florida Library
Jacksonville: Jacksonville Public Library
    Jacksonville University, Swisher Library
    University of North Florida Library
Lake Placid: Archbold Biological Station Library
Lakeland: Lakeland Public Library
Miami: Florida International University Library
    Miami-Dade Public Library
    See also **Coral Gables**
North Miami: Florida International University, Bay Vista Campus
Ocala: Ocala Public Library
Orlando: Orange County Library District
    University of Central Florida Library
Panama City: Bay County Public Library
Pensacola: University of West Florida
St. Petersburg: St. Petersburg Public Library
Sarasota: University of South Florida, Sarasota Campus
    Sarasota County Public Library
Tallahassee: Florida State University Library
    State Library of Florida
    Tallahassee Community College Library

Tampa: Tampa-Hillsborough County Library
    University of South Florida Library
West Palm Beach West Palm Beach Public Library
Winter Park: Rollins College Library

APPENDIX D
TEXT OF FLORIDA LAW REGARDING CAVES AND FOSSILS

Text of current Florida State Statutes regarding fossil collection and cave regulations, speleothems, trespass, etc. follow. This full text includes definitions, regulations and penalties for violations to both public and private property. Please read carefully.

WARNINGS AND RECOMMENDATIONS

240.516 VERTEBRATE PALEONTOLOGICAL SITES AND REMAINS; LEGISLATIVE INTENT AND STATE POLICY.

1) It is the declared intention of the Legislature that vertebrate paleontological sites be protected and preserved and that, pursuant thereto, vertebrate paleontological field investigation activities, including, but not limited to, collection, excavation, salvage, restoration, and cataloging of fossils, be discouraged except when such activities are carried on in accordance with both the provisions and the spirit of this act. However, it is not the intention of the Legislature that the provisions of this act impede mining or quarrying for rock, gravel, fill, phosphate, and other minerals, or the construction of canals or similar excavations, when such activities are permitted by law. Rather, it is the intent of the Legislature that mine and heavy equipment operators be encouraged to cooperate with the state in preserving its vertebrate paleontological heritage and vertebrate fossils by notifying the Florida Museum of Natural History whenever vertebrate fossils are discovered during mining or digging operations and by allowing such fossils to be properly salvaged and that persons having knowledge of vertebrate paleontological sites be encouraged to communicate such information to the museum.

2) It is hereby declared to be the public policy of this state to protect and preserve vertebrate paleontological sites containing vertebrate fossils, including bones, teeth, natural casts, molds, impressions, and other remains of prehistoric fauna, and to provide for the collection, acquisition, and study of the vertebrate fossils of the state which offer documentation of the diversity of life on this planet.

3) It is further declared to be the public policy of the state that all vertebrate fossils found on state-owned lands, including submerged lands and uplands, belong to the state with title to the fossils vested in the Florida Museum of Natural History for the purpose of administration of ss. 240.516-240.5163.
History–ss 1, 2, ch 84-316, s 58, ch 86-163, s 8, ch 88-241.
Note.–Former s. 267.15

240.5161 PROGRAM OF VERTEBRATE PALEONTOLOGY WITHIN FLORIDA MUSEUM OF NATURAL HISTORY.— There is established within the Florida Museum of Natural History a program of vertebrate paleontology, which program has the following responsibilities:

1) Encouraging the study of the vertebrate fossils and vertebrate paleontological heritage of the state and providing exhibits and other educational materials on the vertebrate fauna to the universities and schools of the state.

2) Developing a statewide plan, to be submitted to the director of the Florida Museum of Natural History, for preserving the vertebrate paleontological resources of the state in a

manner which is consistent with the state policies in s. 240-51 and which will not unduly hamper development of this state, including mining and excavating operations.

3) Locating, surveying, acquiring, collecting salvaging, conserving, and restoring vertebrate fossils, conducting research on the history and systematics of the fossil fauna of the state, and maintaining the official state depository of vertebrate fossils.

4) Locating, surveying, acquiring excavating and operating vertebrate paleontological sites and properties containing vertebrate fossils, which sites and properties have great significance to the scientific study of such vertebrate fossils or to public representation of the faunal heritage of the state.

5) Enlisting the aid of professional vertebrate paleontologists, mine and quarry operators, heavy digging equipment operators, and qualified amateurs in carrying out the provisions of subsections (1) through (4), and authorizing their active support and cooperation by issuing permits to them as provided in s. 240.5162.

6) Cooperating and coordinating activities with the 1\ Department of Natural Resources under the provisions of ss. 375.021 and 375.031 and the Department of State under 2\ this chapter in the acquisition, preservation, and operation of significant vertebrate paleontological sites and properties of great and continuing scientific value, so that such sites and properties may be utilized to conserve the faunal heritage of this state and to promote an appreciation of that heritage.

7) Designating areas as "state vertebrate paleontological sites" pursuant to the provisions of this section, which areas are of great and continuing significance to the scientific study and public understanding of the faunal history of the state. However, no privately owned site or grouping of sites shall be so designated without the express written consent of the private owner of the site or group of sites. Upon designation of a state vertebrate paleontological site, the owners and occupants of such site shall be given written notification of such designation by the program. Once such site has been so designated, no person may conduct paleontological field investigation activities on the site without first securing a permit for such activities as provided in s. 240.5162.

8) Arranging for the disposition of the vertebrate fossils by accredited institutions and for the temporary or permanent loan of such fossils for the purpose of further scientific study, interpretative display, and curatorial responsibilities by such institutions.

240.5162 Destruction, purchase, and sale of vertebrate fossils prohibited, exceptions; field investigation permits required; penalty for violation.

1) The destruction, defacement, purchase, and sale of vertebrate fossils found on or under land owned or leased by the state and on land in state-designated vertebrate paleontological sites are prohibited, except that the Florida Museum of Natural History may sell vertebrate fossils and may adopt rules defining "nonessential vertebrate fossils" and prescribing the conditions under which such fossils may be sold or otherwise disposed of by a person holding a permit issued by the Florida Museum of Natural History. Field investigations of vertebrate fossils, including, but not limited to, the systematic collection, acquisition, excavation, salvage, exhumation, or restoration of such fossils, are prohibited on all lands owned or leased by the state and on lands in state-designated vertebrate pale-

ontological sites, unless such activities are conducted under the authority of permits issued by the Florida Museum of Natural History. A permit may be granted by the Florida Museum of Natural History upon application for the permit accompanied by an application fee not to exceed $5 as provided in rules adopted pursuant to s. 240.227 (1) which rules are in furtherance of the preservation of the vertebrate paleontological resources of this state. The privileges authorized pursuant to the grant of a permit as provided in this subsection may not be assigned or sublet to any other party.

2) Any person who, in violation of this section, engages in any of the activities described in subsection (1) without first having obtained a permit to engage in such activity is guilty of a misdemeanor, punishable by a fine not to exceed $500 or by imprisonment in the county jail for a period not to exceed 6 months, or both; and, in addition, he or she shall forfeit to the state all specimens, objects, and materials collected and excavated in violation of this section, together with all photographs and records relating to such materials.

3) The Florida Museum of Natural History may institute a civil action in the appropriate circuit court for recovery of any unlawfully taken vertebrate fossil. The fossil shall be forfeited to the state if the Florida Museum of Natural History shows by the greater weight of the evidence that the fossil has been taken from a particular site within this state and that the person found in possession of the fossil is not authorized by law to possess such fossil.

810.13 Cave vandalism and related offenses.

1) DEFINITIONS—As used in this act:

a) "Cave" means any void, cavity, recess, or system of interconnecting passages which naturally occurs beneath the surface of the earth or within a cliff or ledge, including natural subsurface water and drainage systems but not including any mine, tunnel, aqueduct, or other man made excavation, and which is large enough to permit a person to enter. The word "cave" includes any cavern, natural pit, or sinkhole which is an extension of an entrance to a cave.

b) "Cave life" means any life form which is indigenous to a cave or to a cave ecosystem.

c) "Gate" means any structure or device located to limit or prohibit access or entry to a cave.

d) "Owner" means a person who owns title to land where a cave is located, including a person who holds a leasehold estate in such land, the state or any of its agencies, departments, boards, bureaus, commissions, or authorities, or any county, municipality, or other political subdivisions of the state.

e) "Person" means any individual, partnership, firm, association, trust, corporation, or other legal entity.

f) "Sinkhole" means a closed topographic depression or basin, generally draining underground including but not restricted to, a doline, limesink, or sink.

g) "Speleogen" means an erosional feature of a cave boundary, including, but not restricted to, anastomoses, scallops, rills, flutes, spongework, or pendants.

h) "Speleothem" means a natural mineral formation or deposit occurring in a cave, including but not restricted to, a stalagmite, stalactite, helictite, anthodite, gypsum flower, gypsum needle, angel hair, soda straw, drapery, bacon, cave pearl, popcorn (coral), rimstone, dam, column, or flowstone. Speleothems are commonly composed of calcite, epsomite, gypsum, aragonite, celestite, or other similar minerals.

2) VANDALISM.—It is unlawful for any person, without the prior written permission of the owner to:

a) Break, break off, crack, carve upon, write upon, burn, mark upon, remove, or in any manner destroy, disturb, deface, mar, or harm the surfaces of any cave or any natural material which may be found therein, whether attached or broken, including speleothems, speleogens, or sedimentary deposits. This paragraph does not prohibit minimal disturbance or removal for scientific inquiry.

b) Break, force, tamper with, or otherwise disturb a lock, gate, door, or other obstruction designed to control or prevent access to a cave, even though entrance thereto may not be gained.

c) Remove, deface, or tamper with a sign stating that a cave is posted or citing provisions of this act.

3) CAVE LIFE.—It is unlawful to remove, kill, harm, or otherwise disturb any naturally occurring organism within a cave, except for safety or health reasons. The provisions of this subsection do not prohibit minimal disturbance or removal of organisms for scientific inquiry.

4) POLLUTION AND LITTERING.—It is unlawful to store in a cave any chemical or other material which may be detrimental or hazardous to the cave, to the mineral deposits therein, to the cave life therein, to the waters of the state, or to persons using such cave for any purposes. It is also unlawful to dump, litter, dispose of, or otherwise place any refuse, garbage, dead animal, sewage, trash or other similar waste materials in a cave. This subsection shall not apply to activity which is regulated pursuant to s. 373.106, regarding the intentional introduction of water into an underground formation or chapter 377, regarding the injection of fluids into subsurface formations in connection with oil or gas operations.

5) SALE OF SPELEOTHEMS.—It is unlawful for any person to sell or offer for sale any speleothems in this state or to transport them for sale outside this state.

6) PENALTIES.—Any person who violates subsection (2), subsection (3), subsection (4), or subsection (5) is guilty of a misdemeanor of the first degree, punishable as provided in s. 775.082 or s. 775.083.

INDEX

ABOUT THE AUTHOR

Iris Tracy Comfort has worked as a reporter, editor, and author of scripts for radio and television. A frequent lecturer on writing techniques, she has previously published fiction and educational books, as well as numerous magazine articles. *Florida's Geological Treasures* is her ninth book. She lives in Orlando, Florida.